Detecti...

Ca...

Edinburgh Napier University | THE BIG READ

A Message from the Principal
Edinburgh Napier University

Edinburgh Napier University is professional, ambitious, innovative and inclusive. The #NapierBigRead is a shared reading scheme that exemplifies this. Staff and students will receive a free copy of *Detective McLevy's Casebook* and are encouraged to share thoughts and engage in activities on campus and around Edinburgh. I'm pleased to be able to share this book with you.

McLevy was a detective in Victorian Edinburgh and is said to be the inspiration behind one of our most famous fictional detectives – Sherlock Holmes! It is very likely that while Arthur Conan Doyle was a student here in Edinburgh, he heard stories of the already legendary real-life detective who apparently inspired his now world-renowned character.

It is with continual pride that we watch how our students make a similar impact on society, and how as individuals and part of a collaborative community, you too can be an inspiration to others.

The publication of this edition of *Detective McLevy's Casebook* for the Big Read has been brought to you by students on our publishing course and so in itself is an example of our students' work. We hope that you take inspiration from this to join in with events and even

i

arrange your own, helping to make the Big Read a shared experience that brings together students, staff and the wider community.

These short stories show a different side of Edinburgh and we hope you will use them to explore the city and discover its history. We also hope you will use the book as your passport to meeting more people, making friends and having discussions beyond the classroom.

University is a place where free expression of ideas is encouraged, and again this book provides a wonderful opportunity to explore your ideas with others. So please discuss and examine all the themes and issues that are presented in this book. Perhaps these discussions will help us develop the Big Read in the future – we certainly welcome your thoughts.

We will be holding virtual and live conversations about this book as part of the Edinburgh Napier University Big Read. We also encourage you to think of activities you can organise around *Detective McLevy's Casebook* – perhaps a book club; a debate on our justice system; an author event with modern-day crime writers; a photography competition showing how Edinburgh has changed since the book was written, or even a conversation on how language has evolved. These are just some ideas – we look forward to yours.

You are part of a University community with a truly diverse student population, one where different backgrounds, experiences and opinions are welcomed and valued. At Edinburgh Napier, we want you to achieve your potential and ensure you are well prepared for a range of careers. We recognise that your education is not just about lectures, essays and working in the labs, and we want your experience here with us to be varied and inclusive, and rich with possibilities.

It is easier to take advantage of opportunities when you are supported by a positive community – this is the aim behind the Big Read and why you are being given this book. The Big Read offers you the chance to get involved with students and staff across the University, making new connections and finding new friends. We hope that knowing all our students, and our staff, are reading the same book will strengthen your feeling of being part of our community.

Our community includes students and staff at other institutions and I would like to thank our colleagues at Kingston University in London, who pioneered the Big Read initiative. We have enjoyed collaborating with them as their first Big Read partner and although we have chosen different books this year, our connections remain strong.

I hope you enjoy reading about Detective McLevy's adventures and that your time at Edinburgh Napier University will also be a story you remember fondly.

Yours warmly,

Professor Andrea Nolan
Principal and Vice Chancellor
Edinburgh Napier University

What is the Big Read?

Edinburgh Napier University joined Kingston University as partners of the Big Read in 2016. Before that, Kingston University embarked on a research project into how their first year students spent their spare time, in particular looking at how much they enjoyed reading for pleasure. They had seen whole university pre-arrival reading schemes in the US and were keen to see how they could work in the UK, and in particular impact on the enrolment, engagement and retention of students.

Finding very strong value placed on reading for pleasure amongst those they surveyed, and a general keenness to be involved in shared reading before they got here, they launched their first KU Big Read in 2015.

The effects were immediate – students talked about their pleasure at receiving the book and staff also responded eagerly. Whether or not people had read the book, they were keen to join in the discussion!

This year Edinburgh Napier and Kingston are experimenting with different books, and it will be interesting to see how staff and students of the two universities enjoy being part of a huge book group, with their own bespoke special editions. Again, the two universities will be discussing how to get their whole university involved.

How can I get involved with the Big Read?

It is up to you! We will have lots of activities happening on each campus and around Edinburgh. Follow us on social media to find out more. We also welcome your ideas – just get in touch!

We look forward to seeing how you put your own mark and contribution to the #NapierBigRead. Get involved!

www.NapierBigRead.com
#NapierBigRead

Detective McLevy's Casebook

A Collection of
Crime Stories by

James McLevy

Edinburgh Detective

-m-
MERCHISTON PUBLISHING
www.merchistonpublishing.com

This edition published in 2017
by Merchiston Publishing for the
Edinburgh Napier University Big Read

First published in 2012 by Merchiston Publishing
10 Colinton Road, Edinburgh, EH10 5LG
www.merchistonpublishing.com

**Edited, designed and produced by
Edinburgh Napier University
MSc Publishing students**

A CIP catalogue record for this book
is available from the British Library

Typeset in Baskerville 10.5/13 pt

Printed in Scotland
by Bell & Bain Ltd, Glasgow, G46 7UQ

ISBN: 978-1-911524-00-7

Editor's Note

James McLevy, the son of an Irish weaver, was born in County Armagh, in the late 18th century. By 1833 he had moved to Edinburgh and 'McLevy the Thief-taker', as he became known, was appointed one of the city's first detectives. At that time, Edinburgh was a dangerous place, with pickpockets, prostitutes, vagabonds and, of course, body-snatchers. Only a few years earlier, in 1827–28, two other Irish immigrants, Burke and Hare, had terrorised Edinburgh, murdering at least 16 people. Burke was hanged in 1829, and so strong was the public anger at his crimes that a book was made from his skin, and can be viewed to this day.

McLevy may not have been active in the Burke and Hare case, and this book of his real-crime stories has no such grisly cover, but when he joined the Edinburgh Police in 1830 McLevy would have known of these already notorious murders and been all too aware of the types of criminals he would face over the next three decades. Officially named on Edinburgh City Police's records as their 'number 1' detective, McLevy's cunning mind and scientific methods kept him close on the heels of his targets – and often one step ahead. No wonder he became legendary in his own lifetime and is said to have inspired Arthur Conan Doyle's fictional character, Sherlock Holmes.

After a career spanning over 2,200 cases, McLevy published his short stories in two volumes to popular acclaim. Written from his diaries, and with his own quirky humour and profound humanity, they bring his criminal adversaries to life, even today.

This book collects together stories featured in the original volumes that have never before been published in one collection. The stories provide an insight into the seedy underbelly of Victorian Edinburgh and a tantalizing glimpse into the mind of one of Scotland's pioneering detectives.

Antiquated spellings and punctuation have been retained where appropriate in order to preserve the character of the text, and to respect James McLevy's original words. There is a brief glossary provided at the end for the more obscure terms.

We are grateful to the National Library of Scotland for their invaluable help in acquiring the text. Thanks also to the Edinburgh publishing house, Birlinn Ltd, for their continued co-operation and collaboration. Special thanks go to Iain McIntosh for the stunning cover artwork, and to everyone who has supported our book. We are proud that it has been chosen for the #NapierBigRead.

Contents

The Ingenuity of Thieves

IT WOULD NOT be a hopeful sign of the further triumph of the good principle over the evil if the devil's agents could shew us many examples where they have beaten us, and been enabled to slide clean off the scale. Since my first volume was published, I have been twitted with cases where we have been at fault. I don't deny that there are some, and I will give one or two, of which I have something to say.

In the meantime, I have consolation, not that I have contributed much to the gratifying result in being able to point to the fact, that, since the year 1849, the Reports of the General Board of Prisons have shewn a gradual and steady decrease of the population of our jails. I am free to confess that this result is only, to a small extent, due to us, and the reason is plain enough. The old rebel has had the advantage of us. We have, until very recently, been acting against him on the principle of those masters and mistresses, who, with a chuckle in their hearts, lay pieces of money in the way of suspected servants to catch them, – something in the Twelvetrees way, only they don't wish their unwary victims "to die on the spot;"

nay, having caught them, they only turn them off to rob and steal elsewhere. Yes, in place of our philan-thropists meeting the arch-enemy at the beginning, when he is busy with the young hearts, detecting the first throb of good and turning it to a pulse of evil, we have been obliged to wait until the young sinner was ripe and ready for our hardening mould of punish-ment. There was no Dr Guthrie there – a good way cleverer than the enemy, I suspect, and capable of checkmating him by nipping the canker in the early bud; and then we have been hampered by our legal governors, who have been, and still are, always telling us we must keep a sharp look out for what they call, in their law jargon, an "overt act," the meaning of which, I am informed, is, that we must wait until the rogues are able to do some *clever* thing, sufficient to shew us they have arrived at the age of *discretion,* and become *meritorious* subjects for punishment.

With this advantage over us, it is no great wonder we are sometimes outwitted; nay, the wonder rather is, that we succeed so often as we do, and I think it might be a great consolation to our philanthropists working among the Raggedier ranks, when I tell them, as I have already done, that I don't hold the enemy at so much count as many do. His terrible reputation is due to our own laxity. We let him into the camp, hoof and horns, and then complain that we can't drive or pull him out, whereas we have the power, if we would only exercise it, of *keeping* him out. To my instinctive way of looking at things in those days of improved tactics in war, it seems something like folly to trust to the strength of the wild boar's tail in dragging him out when we can so easily barricade the hole.

Viewing crime even in its diminished extent, there is another consideration which has often opened my eyes pretty wide. We are always a-being told that the human heart has really some good soil in it – (I don't go with those who think that people inherit evil as they do sometimes six toes) – and that, though the devil has always a large granary of tares, we have an abundance of good seed from Jerusalem. I would just ask what use we have been making of that good seed? Have we not been keeping it *in* the bushel just as we keep the light *under* the bushel? In my beat I see a routh of the tares; then I get a sickle put into my hands, and I cut away just as the gardeners do when they prune in order to make the old branches shoot out with more vigour, and, behold, the twisted saplings, how stiff and rigid they become!

But I suspect I am here getting out of my beat. I set out with stating that I had got thrown in my teeth cases where, by the ingenuity of thieves, we have been defeated. They are not cases of mine, anyhow. I may take one or two that relate to one of the most successful artists of the tender sex that ever appeared in Edinburgh, viz., the well-known Jean Brash. I knew her very well, but, strange as it may appear, her ladyship always contrived to keep out of my hands; not that she came always scaithless out of the hands of others, any more than that her victims came without damage out of hers, but that she usually, by her adroit-ness, achieved a miserable success, sufficient to form the foundation of a romantic story. At an early period, she could boast of some attractions, but she could boast more of making these run along with her power of *extraction*; yea, she had three wonderful powers, viz., those of captivating her cullies, retaining them if she chose, and of losing them by capturing their means.

Of the last of these she was more proud than of the others, and if she could, in addition, enjoy the triumph of deceiving an astute constable, she got to the top of her pride – a creature or *fiend*, otherwise strangely formed, for if she seduced and robbed by instinct, she strengthened and justified the inborn propensity by a kind of devil's logic, to the effect that, as she had ruined her immortal soul for the sake of man, she was not only entitled to receive from him the common wages of sin, but also to take from him whatever her subtle fingers could enable her to lay hold of by way of compensation. On one occasion, when, as I think, she resided in the Salt Backet, and when I had occasionally my eye upon her with a look of official love, which she could return with a leer of rather a different kind from that wherewith she wrought her stratagems, she had sallied out, after nightfall, to try her skill on hearts, gold watches, or little bits of bank paper. Doubtless, no more now than on any other occasion, did she imitate the old sirens of whom I have read somewhere. She did not sing them into her toils, that is, her art was not thrown out any more than when a cat purrs at a mousehole. Her power could be in reserve, and yet be available, so that a man in place of being a *dupe,* might flatter himself that he was a *duper* seeking for her charms in the shape of shrinking modesty. So probably thought the happy Mr C——, a mercantile traveller in the hard goods line from Birmingham, but not himself a Brummagem article of false glitter, – a sterling man, if one might judge from the value of the money he carried. In her demureness, Jean appears a real jewel, and he would secure the prize, yet not in the way of an "*un*commercial traveller," for he could and would purchase, and surely in so modest-looking a creature he would make an excellent bargain. Look you, here is a little consolation for us, as we wander about seeking for the vicious to catch them and punish them into virtue. We see occasionally the vicious prowling, in the shades of night, seeking the vicious to deceive them into further vice, and yet sure to be deceived in turn and brought to ruin, while they are trying to make a capital of pleasure out of a poor wretch's necessity. So it has always been: voluptuousness gets hysterical over modesty (Jean Brash's modesty!) and how can we be sorry when we see it choked with the wind-ball of its desire? Then, look ye, is it not a little curious to see vice so conservative of virtue as to become a detective?

Well, Jean is caught by the commercial traveller, how unwittingly the reader may pretty safely guess, and not only caught, but led as a kind of triumph to the Salt Backet, where resides one of those "decent women" who take pity on errant lovers; probably if

Jean had said that the house was her own, he might have doubted of a modesty which could belie itself at home among friends. Then, as they say love has quick wings where there is a shady grove in prospect – not always of sweet myrtle – not seldom of common pine firs, with a good many nettles and thistles growing about the temple – so they were speedily under the auspices of the decent priestess. How long it was before the heart of this lover, which had only been for a little absent from his commercial interests, returned to these so as to make him alive to the conviction that he had been robbed of a hundred-pound Bank of England note, I cannot say, for I was not in this case; but certain it is, that rather quiet part of the town soon echoed to a cry of horror, to the effect that he had been relieved from the anxiety of carrying about with him a bit of paper of that value.

Of all this I have no doubt, because I was perfectly aware that Jean was a woman who could confer the boon of such a relief from anxiety as easily as she could transfer that anxiety to herself; nor could anyone who knew her doubt that she could contrive to make the care a very light one. Even the more romantic part of the story which "illustrates" the memory of this remarkable woman, I have no proper right to gainsay – how the commercial traveller rushed downstairs and bawled out at the top of his English voice for a constable – how the constable made his appearance while the traveller kept watch at the door – how they hurried upstairs to seize when they should discover the money – how they found Jean quite in an easy state of conscious innocence – how she adjured the constable to search the house and her own body, and satisfy himself that the unfortunate man was in error – how, for that purpose, she quietly handed to him a lighted candle placed in a brass candlestick, and well fixed there by a round of paper not to oscillate in the way of unsteady lights – how the constable searched for the missing note with this candle, so fixed by the paper roll at the end thereof, all the while that Jean was muttering to herself, "The fool has taken the wrong end" – how he failed in his search, and how the traveller gave up all hope, if he did not suspect that he had lost his note elsewhere, and therefore resolved to avoid the fearful exposure of committing the woman – and how Jean was at length left quietly in her state of innocence. The reader may guess that Jean at her own time undid the piece of paper from the end of the candle, thus rescuing the "Governor and Company of the Bank of England" from their temporary degradation, and enjoying a quiet chuckle at her successful ingenuity.

Now, I confess I never liked very well to hear this romantic bit of Jean's history, and simply for this reason, that I was not there to hold the candle.

On another occasion – though I am bound to say I have heard the credit of the adventure ascribed to a young unfortunate of the name of Catherine Brown, who lived in Richmond Street – our Jean was pursuing her *nomade* vocation in Princes Street. The night was dark enough, and the hour late enough, to inspire adventurers with sufficient confidence to flirt a little with the coy damsel, without being detected by curious friends. There are always numbers of these shy and frolic-some fish who are fond of poking their noses into the dangerous meshes, without any intention of entering the seine, where they would be pretty sure to be caught. The regular tramps, such as our heroine, are quite up to these amateurs, hate them heartily, and sometimes make them pay, and very deservedly too, golden guineas for silvern words. I can't say I have much sympathy for them when they fall into misfortune, and ask our help to get money restored to their pockets, which pockets they voluntarily placed within the range of curious fingers. Why, if these fingers are delicate enough to be fondled and kissed without recompense, the men shew a bad grace in complaining that the same fingers fondled in their turn a bit of gold or paper supposed to be beyond their reach. Of course we do our duty, but always with a feeling in such cases that the victims did not do theirs, and impose upon us the trouble of rectifying the results of their folly, if not vice. Such fire-ships shew enough of light to enable these gay yachtmen to steer sufficiently aloof. (Were I able to be fanciful myself, I would not need to borrow the words of one of our well-read Lieutenants.) These young men play round the rancid candlelight of impurity, which at once enables them to see reflected in their self-conceit their immunity from danger, and imparts a little heat to their imagination. Rather fine language for me, but I see the sense of it.

With one of these gaudy night-moths our famous heroine had forgathered; and thinking probably that if he did not choose to consider her soft hand sacred from his squeeze, she was not bound to esteem his pocket tabooed against the prying curiosity of her fingers, she made free with the contents thereof. At least the youth thought so; for on the instant he bawled out to the passing bull's-eye that he had been robbed. The constable, who knew Jean – as who didn't – immediately laid hold of her, and as there were no passers-by to complicate the affair, the money would of course be got upon the instant. It was no less than a five-pound note, at least so said the young man; but Jean, whose coolness never forsook her, simply denied the charge.

It was a matter of short work for the constable to search her so far as he could, – an act in which he was helped by the young man. Her pockets were turned out, but with the exception of a scent-bottle, a white handkerchief, and some brown pawn-tickets, nothing was found there. All round the pavement the light of the lantern shewed nothing in the shape of the valuable bit of paper, and there was no sympathiser to whom she could have handed it.

"You must be under a delusion," said the policeman.

"Impossible!" cried the youth. "There are as many folds in a woman's dress as there are loops and lies in her mind. March her up."

To all which Jean replied with her ordinary laugh of consummate self-possession, if not impudence. Nor was she at all unwilling to march – rather the contrary.

She knew what she was about.

"Come away," she said, "and we shall see who is right and who is wrong."

And so away they went. Nor was it long before Jean was examined by one of the female searchers of the Office. No five-pound note was found upon her; and though the young man raved incessantly about the absolute certainty of the theft, the policeman, and not less the lieutenant on duty, was satisfied that there must have been a mistake, – a conclusion which the redoubted Jean confirmed by a cool declaration, in all likelihood false, that she had seen the young gentleman in the company of not less scrupulous women a very short time before. There was only one thing to be done – to set Jean free.

"And who is to pay me for all this time?" said she, as she turned to the lieutenant a face in which was displayed a mock seriousness, contrasting vividly with the wild, anxious countenance of the youth. "I could have made five pounds in the time in an honest way, so that I am the real loser; and who, I ask again, is to pay me?"

A question to which she no more expected a reply than she did the payment of her lost gains in an honest way. And with head erect, if not indeed with an air of injured innocence, she marched out of the Office. Yet nothing would satisfy the young man that he had not been robbed; and he too, when he saw that he had no hope, left with the conviction that he was a greatly injured innocent.

The matter died away, leaving only the impression of some unaccountable mistake or indetectible priggery, though probably the presumption was against the woman, whose genius in this peculiar line of art was known to be able to find her advantage in a mystery through which the most practised eye of official vision could see nothing.

A day or two passed. No more was heard of the young man, who no doubt had made up his mind to the loss of the five pounds; nor did the constable, who was again upon his beat about the same hour, think anymore of the mystery, unless perhaps the place brought up a passing thought of wonder how the bit of paper could have disappeared in so very short a time. A woman came running up to him. It was Jean, and she was all of a bustle. Laying hold of the man by the left hand –

"What now," said the constable, who knew well that something not altogether useless to Jean was coming. "In one of your high jinks?"

"No; I have a secret for you, man."

"What is it?"

"Oh, you're such a peaching fellow, one can hardly speak with you. Would you like the young sprig's five-pound note? He can't afford to lose it, and my conscience is queezy."

"Ah, ha!" cried the constable, "Jean Brash's conscience!"

"Aye, man, even Jean Brash's conscience," replied she, a little grandly. "A queer thing maybe, but still a thing. Aye, man, I would tell you where the five-pound note is if you would keep me out of the gleg's claws."

"Well, I will," replied he, getting into official cunning. "Tell me where the note is, and I will do my best for you."

"Ah, I know you won't, and so I can't trust you with an admission which you would use against me; but suppose I were to make a sign, eh? A nod is as good, you know, as —"

"Well, well, give me the nod to lead me to the note."

"And you will say nothing? Well, who's your tailor?" she cried, laughing.

"What has that to do with the note?" responded the man.

"Something that may astonish you," said she, as she still held his arm, and fumbled about the cuff of his coat. "He gives you a deep cuff. Very convenient as a kind of wee pawn."

"Nonsense. Get off. You are trifling."

"Not just," she replied, again laughing and thrusting her nimble fingers, so like instruments of legerdemain, deep into the cuff – "not just. Suppose you were to find the note in here after I am gone, would you just say you got it there, and nothing of me?"

"Perhaps I would."

"Then search your cuff," she cried, swinging his arm to a side, "and you will find it."

And running away, she threw behind her the words: "But be sure and act honourably, and give it to the prig."

The constable was a little confused, but he did not fail to begin to search the cuff, from which Jean, while pretending she had deposited the £5 in the receptacle, had absolutely extracted the spoil, – the identical note which she had placed there at the instant of her seizure on the night it was stolen, and which he had carried about with him for two days, altogether unconscious of the valuable deposit.

The man could swear, as in a rage he searched and found nothing, but he couldn't detect, and I don't think he ever knew the trick played off upon him; for it came out long afterwards when Jean was safe, and in one of her fits of bragging, how she did the authorities.

These are not *my* experiences, and I can give no guarantee of their truth; but, as I have said, I should have liked to be the man who held the candle, supported in the socket by such a valuable bit of paper; and I must add, that I should have liked also to be the man who wore the coat with the deep cuff.

So much for such talk as goes on amongst us. But I have had enough experience of Jean to enable me to say that she was the most "organic thief" of my time. So much was her *make* that of a thief, that I doubt whether training in a ragged school would have had much effect upon her. The house she occupied in James' Square was a "bank of exchange," regularly fitted up for business. In the corner of a door-panel of every bedroom, there was a small hole neatly closed up with a wooden button, so as to escape all observation. Then the lower panels were made to slide, so that while through the peep she could see when the light was extinguished, she could by the opened panel creep noiselessly in on all fours and take the watch off the side-table, or rifle the pockets of the luckless wight's dress. She made occasionally great catches, having once "done" £400; but she was at length "done" by the paltry sum of 7s. 6d. I have heard that she is still alive in Australia, and married, perhaps driving, like a pastoral Arcadian, "the yowes to the knowes".

The Orange Blossom

HOWEVER ASSIDUOUSLY I have plied my vocation, I
have never thought that I was doing the good which
our masters expect of us in stopping the sliders on
the slippery scale of criminal descent. They only
commence again, and when they slide off altogether others rise to run the same course. If I have taken
credit for a diminution, I suspect that Dr Guthrie has
had more to do with it than I. Sometimes I have had
qualms from a conviction that I have been hard on
many who could scarcely be said to be responsible. I
have been, no doubt, often an unwelcome intruder
upon merry-makings and jollifications, but then it may
be said for me that these merry-makers were merry
at the expense of others. Well, "you have stopped
marriages where one of the parties was innocent."
True, but the innocent party was attracted by the glitter
of stolen gold, and why should a resetting bridegroom
escape a loss any more than a resetting pawnbroker? A
dowried thief in stolen orange blossom may be a pretty
object to a loving snob – to me, however, she is nothing
else but a thief, and if I am bound to tear her from his
arms, I have just the satisfaction that I transfer her to

the arms of justice, who will hug her a good deal closer.

In 1842, our Office was inundated with complaints of house enterings by false keys. There had been no fewer than sixteen in six weeks, and not a trace could be discovered.

"Why, McLevy," said the lieutenant one day to me, "we will lose caste. Aberdeen will mock us, and Berwick hold up the finger at us. What's to be done?"

"There's a difficulty," replied I. "In the first place, I am satisfied there is only one thief; in the second place, there is only one place of deposit; in the third place, I am only one man; and, in the fourth place, I am not an angel. Yet, notwithstanding, I have a hope."

"What is it founded on?"

"This little bit of swatch," replied I, shewing him a paring of print not larger than two crown pieces.

"Why do you place faith in a rag like that?"

"I got it," replied I, "from Mrs ——, the proprietor of a house in Richmond Street, the last one operated on, and Mrs Thick, the broker in the Cowgate, thinks she might be able to match it."

"That promises something."

"I think I have the sex too," said I, with an intention to be jocular.

"Man or woman?"

"Woman," replied I.

"Oh, something peculiarly in the female line," said he. "I hope not an object in the *greening* way?"

"No; something preparatory to, and going before that. Can't you guess?"

"No – yes – let me see – orange blossom?"

"Yes, orange blossom," said I. "The thief wants to be married. She has laid in the dowry from the same house in Richmond Street, and finished off with the bride's badge."

Our conversation terminated with a laugh, for, after all, we were scarcely serious, and I repaired to Mrs Thick, a fine specimen of her class, who, rather than pocket a penny from stolen goods, would have surrendered her whole stock, amounting to hundreds of pounds.

As I went along I continued my former ruminations on this wonderful succession of robberies. That they were all done by one hand I had, as I have said, little doubt; but, considering the short period of time, the difficulty of watching and accomplishing even one house, the multiplied chances of being seen, the obstructions of locks, the accidents so rife in pledging or disposing by sale, the many inquiries and investigations that had already been made by sharp people, I could not help being filled with admiration at a dexterity so unexampled in my experience. And then, if I was right in my whimsical conjecture as to sex, what a wonderful creature of a woman she must be!

"She is worthy of me anyhow," I said to myself; and as we illiterate people are fond of a pun, I added, just for my own ear, "I will catch her through *thick* or *thin*."

Now, don't be angry at my wit; it is better than you think; for don't you remember of one of the name of Thin, with the three balls above his door?

And not insensible to the effect of my solitary effort

at being clever out of my sphere, I entered the shop of the broker.

"Now, Mrs Thick," said I, "have you got a match for my swatch?"

"Indeed I think I have," replied the good woman, although she knew she would in all likelihood be a heavy loser by her honesty. "Here's the gown," and, taking the pattern out of my hand, "see it's just the thing – aye, just a bit o' the self-same. Whaur in a' the warld got ye the swatch? Surely it's no canny to meddle wi' you, you're an awfu' man; but, do ye ken, I canna think after a' that that gown was stown."

"I never said it was, Mrs Thick."

"Aye, but it's a sign o' dead hens when the farmer rins after the fox that has loupit the yett."

"And I never said it was not," replied I, for I had reasons to be cautious.

"Weel, to be honest, Mr McLevy, I really dinna think it was."

"And why?"

"Just because it was brought to me by that industrious creature Lizzy Gorman."

"That's the handsome hawker, as the young chaps call her?" said I.

"Just the same."

"And what makes you have so much faith in Elizabeth?"

"Just because I have kent her for years; and naebody could look into her bonny face, sae simple and sweet, without being sure she's an honest creature. Then she has hawked sae lang through Edinburgh, that had she been dishonest, she would hae been fund oot."

"Well, she does look like an honest girl," said I. "Have you had many articles from her besides the gown?"

"Just a heap," replied she. "But ken ye what, Mr McLevy?"

"If I knew the what, I could perhaps tell," said I, keeping my friend in humour.

"This is Elizabeth's marriage-day," she whispered in my ear.

"Orange blossom!" muttered I.

"Aye, orange blossom," repeated Mrs Thick; "Lizzy's as far up as even that."

Now I had no wish that Mrs Thick should have heard my muttering, but the answer satisfied me I had muttered to some purpose.

"And who is the happy man?" inquired I, though I would not have given the sprig of orange blossom for the other sprig.

"Just a snab," replied she; "but then Elizabeth has money, and a full house, a' by her ain industry, and she says she'll set him up."

"Well, the affair looks promising," said I, adding, as I meditated a little, "unless the swine runs through it."

"Oh, it's ower near now for the sow; you're no Scotch and maybe dinna ken the auld rhyme –

> *'Lang to woo, and then to marry,*
> *That's the way to mak' things miscarry;*

> *But first to marry, and then to woo,*
> *Is the surest way to keep out the sow.'*

Aye, the beast seldom comes on the marriage-day to scatter the ribbons and the orange blossom."

"Not sure," said I, somewhat absent. "But letting the marriage of this most industrious girl alone, I have a favour to ask of you. Will you take care of this gown, and all the other articles Elizabeth has brought to you?"

"I will," replied she; "but the Lord kens how I'm to get them a' collected. There's a cart-load o' them; but I hae nae fear they're a' honestly come by."

"I hope so," said I, as I left the shop, with the intention of returning to the Office for a list of the property stolen from the sixteen houses, and then perhaps to call and see the bonny bride.

And as I went along, I began to gather up the fragments of my prior knowledge of my handsome hawker. She was pretty well known for several peculiarities. Her face was that of a gipsy, with the demureness of the race mixed with a simplicity which they seldom exhibit; and her dress, plain almost to Quakerism, had all that dandyism which extreme care and an excellent taste can bestow on very plain things. Quite an exception to the crowd of town-hawkers, she was far above their baskets and bundles of troggan. We see these every day. Some are enveloped in a mountain of shining articles of tin, – others are surrounded with a whole forest of wicker-work in the shape of baskets and reticules, – others rejoice in a heap of black tin shovels, – many are devoted to kitchens, where they shew their white caps to the servants out of a basket neatly covered with a white towel, – the apple and orange troggars are everywhere, the red-herring female merchants being probably at the foot of the tree. Despising all these, Elizabeth was seldom burdened with more than a neat paper parcel. Even that she was often without, and indeed I had heard it often remarked that no one knew what she hawked. Yet the readiness with which she was admitted at pretty high doors was remarkable, and once in, the secret article, probably drawn from under her gown, was an easy sale – at to her, no doubt, a remunerating price – under the charm of a winning simplicity, aided by the ready tale of the interesting orphan. A little consideration of these things soon brought me to the conclusion that it was only by such an adept, thoroughly acquainted with the inside of so many houses, by means of a daring eye and a quick ear, that all these sixteen entries in six weeks could have been effected. Nor would it be too much to say that the orange blossom was not accidental, if it was an object which she had known to be in the house where a marriage was on the *tapis*, and of which she had obtained the knowledge by a prior visit.

I had now got thoroughly interested in my pretty hawker. Her movement on the scale was now upwards. It is seldom that thieves slide up to Hymen's bower; and if I had had no other motive than simply to see the young woman who could perform such miracles, I would have gone twenty miles to see her in her marriage dress, orange blossom, and all. I soon got my list completed; indeed, I was now somewhat in a hurry. The apathy with which the lieutenant had charged me was changed into enthusiasm. Strange perversity of the human heart! I felt a jealousy of the snab. He was unworthy of such perfection. The bride must be mine at all hazards, even if I should be obliged to renounce my beauty to the superior claims of the Colonial Secretary.

Having got my list, I made again for the Cowgate, where, as I passed the stair-foot leading to the room of the intended, I saw the beginnings of the crowd which was to honour this match between the son of Crispin and the daughter surely of that famous goddess who got her skeleton keys from Vulcan for a kiss. I would pay due attention to the crowd by and by, and gratify it perhaps more than by the raree-show it was gaping to see. It was Mrs Thick I was now after; and having again found her at her old post, I went over with her as quickly as I could the long list, and became quite satisfied that her estimate of a cart-load was not much below the mark.

"Now, you are upon your honour," said I to her. "You must be careful to retain all those articles for an hour or so, for I am sorry to inform you I must take them from you."

"And can it be possible!" she exclaimed, no doubt with reference to the guilt of her industrious protégé;

and then relaxing into a kind of smile, "Surely, surely you're no to act the animal we were speaking of. The bride's dressed, the bridegroom is up, the minister is waited for, and the crowd is at the door. Poor Lizzy, poor Lizzy, could ever I have thought this of you!"

"Well, I admit that I intend to be at the marriage anyhow," said I. "They have not had the grace to invite me; but I am often obliged to overlook slights from my friends."

And leaving my honest broker in the very height of her wonder – if not with uplifted hands and open mouth – I made my way to the house of rejoicing, shaded as all such are with that quiet decorum, if not solemnity, which the black coat and white cravat have such a power of casting over leaping hearts and winged hopes. The crowd had by this time increased; and among the rest was my assistant waiting for me – though ostensibly there to overawe the noisy assemblage. The Irish boys and girls were predominant, shouting their cries, among which "The snab and the hawker, hurra," would not sound as an honour upstairs. When I say Irish boys and girls, I mean to include adults of sixty, grim and shrivelled enough in all save the heart, which is ever as young and green as an urchin's. Then who does not feel an interest in the evergreen of marriage, albeit its red berries are often full of bitterness and death? The young look forward to it, and the old back upon it – the one with a laugh, the other with a sigh; but the interest is ever the same. Nay, I'm not sure if the sigh has not a little hope in it, even to that last dripping of the sands, when even all other "pleasure has ceased to please". Excuse me, it is not often I have to sermonise on marriage, except those between the law and vice, where the yoke is not a pleasant one, and yet perhaps less unpleasant than many of those beginning with love on the one side, and affection on the other. And now I am the detective again.

"Are the constables ready?" I whispered to my assistant.

"Yes; they're in the stair-foot beyond the meal shop on the other side."

"Then keep your post, and have an eye to the window."

"For *ha'pennies?*" said he, with a laugh.

"I'm just afraid I may reduce the *happiness*," replied I, not to be outdone in Irish wit on a marriage occasion, however bad at it.

And pushing my way among the noisy crowd, whose cry was now "McLevy!" "He's to run awa' wi' the bride!" "The snab has stown his varnished boots!" "The bride is to sleep in a police cell!" and so forth, I mounted the stair till I came to the marriage-hall. Uninvited as I was, I made "no gobs," as they say, at entering, but, opening the door, stood there among the best of them. A more mysterious guest perhaps never appeared at a marriage before since the time of the famous visitor at Jedburgh, where the king danced; but I had no attention to bestow on expressions of wonder. The scene was of a character to be interesting enough to anyone. To me the chief object of attention was the head of the bride, where the orange blossom ought to be; and there to be sure it was, set off, as it ought to have been, with green myrtle. With this I was so much occupied, that I cannot say it was just then that I scanned Elizabeth's dress – a fine lavender glacé silk, adorned with as many knots as would have bound all the lovers in the room in silken bands; collar and sleeve of lace, of what kind goes beyond my knowledge; grey boots, necklace, and armlets; white kid-gloves, with no doubt a good many rings under them. These notices came rather afterwards, my practical eye ranging meanwhile – the party being dead silent as yet – round the room, where, according to my recollection of my list, I saw a perfect heaping up of all manner of things collected from the sixteen opened houses, which the pretty bride had so industriously entered.

My survey was the result of a few rapid glances, and I recurred to the parties. The amazement was just at its height, yet strange to say the only one who stood there unmoved, and with no greater indication of internal disturbance than a cast-down eye, overshaded by its long lashes, was Elizabeth Gorman. That she understood the object of my visit I had no doubt; nor was I surprised that a creature of her nerve, capable of what she had done, should stand before me in the midst of all her friends – and in the presence of her intended husband – as immoveable as a lump of white marble; no additional paleness, no quiver of the lip, no hairbrained glances of fear.

"And who are you?" at last cried the souter *futur*; "you are not invited."

"No; I have taken the liberty to come uninvited," replied I, as I threw my eye over the body of the young snab arrayed in absolute perfection, from the glossy cravat to the shining boots, so spruce and smart that the taste of Elizabeth must have been at the work of preparation. Nor was he without some right, if one might judge the number of houses laid under contribution for a dowry which was to be his, and by the help of which he was to become a master.

Whereupon there arose a perfect Babel of voices – "No right;" "McLevy has no right here;" "Turn him out."

To all this I paid little attention; I was more curious about a movement on the part of Elizabeth, whose right hand was apparently fumbling about her pocket. A pocket in a bride's dress! – ay, just so. Elizabeth Gorman was a bride of a peculiar kind; she had a *pocket* even as a part of her bridal apparel, and there was more there than a cambric handkerchief.

"I will help you to get out your napkin, Elizabeth," said I.

And putting my hand into the sacred deposit, I pulled out two check-keys. With these two keys, she had opened (I speak in anticipation) the whole sixteen houses.

I managed this movement in such a manner that I believe no one could know what I abstracted except Elizabeth herself, who seemed to care no more for the discovery than she had as yet done for any part of the ceremony.

"And the orange blossom," said I, "I have a fancy for this too," I said, as I, very gently I hope, took off the wreath, and, in spite of the necessary crumpling of so expressive an emblem of bliss, put it in my pocket.

The hubbub was now general, and Crispin thinking that his honour was touched, waxed magniloquent. He even put himself into a fighting attitude, and sparred away with all the valour of a gentleman called upon to protect injured innocence. Nor Dowsabell, nor Dulcinea, nor any other heroine of romance, had ever so formidable a champion; but then I did not choose to take up the snab's gage. I contented myself with stepping between one or two of the guests to the window, gave two or three knocks, and then took up my station by the side of Elizabeth. The door opened, and in came my assistant.

"I choose to claim this young woman for my bride," I said, with a little of an inward chuckle. "I will dispose of her property; meanwhile, all of you leave the room. Clear out, officer," I added, as they seemed to loiter and murmur.

And so to be sure, my assistant, to make short work of emptying the room, hurried them off, the last loiterer being the snab, whose look at Elizabeth carried as much of what is called sentiment as might have touched even her, who, however, received the appeal with the same cold indifference she had exhibited all through the strange scene. I do not say she did not feel. It is hardly possible to suppose that a young woman dressed for marriage, and in the hands of the police, with banishment before and shame behind, could be unmoved; but the mind of these creatures is so peculiarly formed that they make none of nature's signs, and are utterly beyond our knowledge. That something goes on within, deep and far away from even conjecture, we cannot doubt; but it is something that never has been known, and never will be, because they themselves have no words and no symbols to tell what it is.

When thus left alone with her, it might have been expected that she would give me some token that she was *human*, but no; there she stood in all her finery, unmoved and immoveable, her gipsy face calm, if not placid, her eye steady, and without uttering a single word.

"And now, Elizabeth," I said, "I daresay you know the reason of this intrusion; you are accused of having entered no fewer than sixteen dwelling-houses, and stealing therefrom many valuables, and I must apprehend you."

"Very well."

"Have you any more keys than those I have got?"

"No more."

"Were these all you used?"

"You can find that out; I confess nothing."

"Well, then, make yourself ready to go with me; get your shawl and bonnet."

And without further sign of being even touched with any feeling of remorse or shame, she proceeded calmly to put on these articles of dress.

"I am ready."

"Too serious," thought I, as I looked to a side-table and saw the wine and the cake. I wanted to give things a more cheerful look.

Was ever a bride taken away without the "stirrup-cup", even a glass of her own wine?

But no, it wouldn't do. Elizabeth would neither take nor give, and so I, too, went without my glass.

"Keep the house," said I to my assistant, "till I return. I will post the constables at the foot of the stairs."

And, taking Elizabeth by the arm, I sallied forth amidst a noise that roused the whole Cowgate; and no wonder, perhaps such a scene was never witnessed there before, certainly not since. Mrs Thick's hands were uplifted as we passed; nor was the wonder less among the other neighbours, who looked upon Elizabeth as a pattern of industry and strict behaviour.

After depositing my bride I got arrangements made for clearing the house of the stolen property. Everything was removed except the table, chairs, and frame of the bed, and pages would not contain a catalogue of the fruits of this young woman's industry. But the recovery from Mrs Thick was a different process. I was up till four in the morning getting out and identifying the numerous articles of all kinds stored away in her premises.

By and by, my bride was tried before the High Court; and here I may be allowed a remark on the apparent callosity of people of her stamp. I have often noticed that these dumb, impassable victims are more ready at the end to give way than your loquacious asserters of innocence. I take this peculiarity for a proof that they bleed inwardly, and that while we are angry with them for being what we call unnatural, they are paying the forfeit in another shape. This extraordinary girl, after all her silence and apparent indifference, pled guilty to ten different cases of house-entering, and they were all effected by the two keys I took out of her pocket at the scene of the contemplated marriage. Fourteen years' transportation was her punishment, and she heard the sentence without a sigh or a tear.

I need scarcely add that this was the only thief I ever discovered through the means of orange blossom.

The Half-Crowns

I HAVE OFTEN THOUGHT we are a little mole-eyed in
social questions. How much were we to have paid the
devil for our letting in mental food to the people, for
the introduction of machinery, for giving up hanging
poor wretches! And yet we have paid him nothing, – all
movements coming to a poise. When I lay hold of a
robber by the throat, we have a tussle, but it does not
last long. Either he or I may be down; we don't murder
each other; the forces destroy themselves, and there's
peace. Where is all the expected crop of forgeries and
coinings that were to spring up under the spread of
the guano of education? The art of learning to write
was to be the learning to forge, and electro-plating
(if I can spell it) was to turn off half-crowns by the
thousand. Nothing of all this. The people are better
fed, the working men better employed, fewer murders,
fewer forgeries, fewer coinings. I think we have rather
taken from his majesty below, and I suspect he is
fretful. What a fury we would put him in were we to
take the young from him, of whom, in a certain class,
he has had the charge since Adam coined that bad
penny, Cain!

So I thought, when I told the story of the pewter spoons. I thought I had not another case of coining in my books; but I find I was wrong. Not long ago, in November 1858, I happened (I was always happening) to meet, at the foot of the stair leading to Ashley Buildings, in Nether Bow, near John Knox's Church, a clot of little boys and girls busy looking at some wonderful things, with eyes as bright and round as a new-turned-out shilling. On bending my head over the little people, and directing my eyes down through the midst of them, I found that the objects of their delight were a number (turned out to be a dozen) of beautiful glittering half-crowns and florins, all new from the mint. Was ever a nest of Raggediers shone upon with a blaze of such glory! Did ever her Majesty's face appear so beautiful to any of her loyal subjects!

On inquiry, I found that the urchins, when playing in the stair of Ashley Buildings, had found the pieces secreted in the corners of two window-soles. They were placed outside, so that any person going up the stair could reach them without entering any of the flats. I examined the places of deposit under the direction of my leaders – six of the pieces were on the window-sole of the first flat, and the other six on that of the highest. Then they had been cunningly placed in small-scooped crevices, close by the rybats. On coming down with my coins in my hand, and my troop around me, all chattering and vindicating their rights to the waifs, I was a little taken aback by the appearance of two ladies coming up the dark, dingy stair.

At the first glance, and under the impression of the rustle of their heavy silk skirts, I took them for philanthropical grandees from the New Town on a visit of mercy to the hags of Ashley Land; and no wonder, for the very gayest of our crinolined nymphs, so far as regarded silk velvet and ribbons, were not qualified to tie the latchet of one of their boots. Nor was my impression changed when, standing to a side to give space to the swirl of their wide skirts, as well as honour to their progress, I looked respectfully, if not with a little awe (not much in my way) into their faces, – delicate, pretty, genteel, nor with a single indication of the flaunting lightness sometimes, in my experience, accompanying, but not adorning very gay attire.

On ascending two steps above me, one of them turned round, and, with an inquiring gaze, asked what was the matter, in a clear, bell-like voice, which was to me at the moment perhaps the more musical, because it came from such a delicate throat: but the speech was English, and we want that *spoken* music in Scotland, – at least there's not much of it among the denizens of Ashley Land.

"A little row among the boys," said I, just as a suddenly rising thought suggested something, – I won't say what.

"He's ta'en our half-croons, mem," cried a bantam, whose windpipe I could have squeezed.

Upon hearing which, my ladies turned somewhat abruptly, and proceeded downstairs. I could even fancy that the noise of their silks was increased by a flurry, – a movement altogether which I could not, even with the aid of my sudden thought, very well understand. On getting to the foot of the stair, and quit of my brawlers, I observed my two damsels walking majestically up the High Street, as if they had utterly forgotten their visit of mercy, for which their purses, and probably their Bibles, had been put in preparation. I had intercepted grace, condescension, and mercy, even when about to light, like ministering angels, on the hearts and homes of the miserable. Well, another time – mercy is long-suffering.

Just as I thus found myself a little satirical perhaps, up comes the man Richardson, who lived in Ashley Buildings.

"It's not often," said he, "that folks like me and my wife have lodgers in our small room like yon," pointing in the direction of my ladies.

"Like whom?" said I.

"Why, did you not see them coming out of our stair?"

"Yes, I saw two ladies superbly dressed; who are they?"

"Just my lodgers; your common lodging-house keepers can't touch that, I think."

"Why, no," said I; "but you haven't told me who or what they are."

"That's a hard question," replied he; "I can only say they are English, very polite, and pay their score."

"Any more?" said I; for although I had no doubt of the man's honesty, I did not wish to be forward with my half-crowns, as a "let up" in the first instance.

"Why, we are not sure of them," said he. "They are the strangest customers we ever had. They keep their door shut, and every second day there comes to them a man, as much a tailor and jeweller-made swell in his way as they are in theirs. Then the door is still more sure to be locked, and the keyhole screened."

"Did you ever hear his name?"

"Oh, yes – Mr Harvey."

"And theirs?"

"Miss Matilda Jerome and Miss Elizabeth Jackson."

"Is he English too?" inquired I.

"Yes, of the highest tone, but very condescending. He asks Mrs Richardson how she does, and she says, 'Quite well, I thank you, sir;' but this doesn't prevent her, you know, from sometimes trying a *chink* – the *keyhole* is an impossibility."

"And what has she seen?"

"Not much yet. The little is strange. The great Mr Harvey, the moment he gets in, takes off his fine suit and his rings, and puts on a fustian jacket and breeches. They work at something requiring a great deal of the fire, and then we hear *birrs*, and *clanks*, and *whizzes* – what you might expect where some small machinery is in gear."

"Producing, perhaps," said I, "something like *that*?" shewing him a half-crown piece.

"Our very suspicion," replied he, as he took the piece into his hand, and seemed to wonder at the "turn out" of his little room. "But where got you it?"

"With eleven more, on two of the window-soles of your staircase."

"Hidden there by them?"

"I can't say," replied I; "but hark ye, when would be the best time for me to see the ladies and Mr Harvey together – if in the fustian, so much the better?"

"Tomorrow forenoon," replied he. "They are all on the *stravaig* today."

"Well, in the meantime, Richardson, you are mum."

"Dumb."

And leaving my useful informant, I proceeded on my way, ruminating as usual. It didn't need a witch to tell the intention of the deposit, or the place selected for it. The false money would, of course, be dangerous in their room, and even in their pockets it would be imprudent to have more at a time than perhaps the single piece they were trying to utter. The deposit was thus a little outside bank, from which the three might severally supply themselves any number of times a day; and though the bank stood a chance of being broken, they could lose nothing, while there would always be the difficulty of connecting them with it either as *depositors* or *drawers*. The scheme exhibited at least adroitness enough to satisfy me that the three were experienced hands. And yet, just observe the insanity of crime, whereby it renders itself a fool to itself. These clever people, no doubt, never thought that their splendid dresses, their engrossing admiration of their persons, and their exacting claims on the attention of those who would have been very willing to pass them by, only tended to the sharpening of official vision.

On making some inquiries at the Office, I learned that from what we knew as yet of the great Mr Harvey, there could be little doubt that he was a personage who for years had been driving the same trade in the south of England, where he had been often in trouble, and where not less than in London he was reputed as the best "coiner" in the kingdom. His companions were also known as adepts, whose beauty and accomplishments in another peculiar line enabled them to help the common store. Nor was Harvey limited to one department alone, being as well adapted and inclined for *taking* good money as for *coining* or uttering bad; so that viewing them as possessed of these three sources of income, we need not be astonished at their personal equipment. How little people know of the money that passes, like water over stones, through the hands of such gentry! The swell is talked of as a poor devil, with stolen finery, who lives merely in that sense from hand to mouth, which implies only freedom from want. A swell is not thus made up or maintained. It is an expensive character. The hunger and burst may haunt him as an inevitable condition; but as is the hunger, so is the burst with them – an extravagance this latter that would provoke the envy of many a fast youth, born in a mansion, and who runs through his property as fast as the horse he rides. I am speaking of England. It is seldom that we have the pleasure of seeing the true grandee here. Scotland is too poor for them. Yet I have sometimes caught them grazing on our lean turnips, when the English fields were infested with these foxes, the detectives.

So I had got on my beat no fewer than three swells, and surely a hunter of sorry thieves like me behoved to be on my honour. There is, I understand, a difficult etiquette how to *approach* the great, and how to *recede*, without shewing to their circumcised eyes the back part of your person. Would I not require a lesson to save me from being dishonoured and disgraced by some offence against the code of genteel behaviour? Might they not smile at my Scotch bluntness and vulgarity, and refuse obedience to a baton of Scotch fir? One consolation at least – if the *rose* is for polite nostrils, the *thistle* is for thin skins. I scarcely think that I tried a rehearsal that night; but I was saved from all fears by my hope of being received by my great man in a fustian jacket: and as for the ladies, they might consider an Earlston gingham or a Manchester print sufficient for the trade of melting and silvering.

Next day I was on my watch, when about twelve o'clock I saw my great man enter the stair-foot of Ashley Buildings. The glance I got of him satisfied me that Richardson had not exaggerated his grandeur. Everything on him was of the best, and the jemmy cane shewed the delicacy of the hand by which it was held, and by which, too, it was made to go through those exquisite twirls, so expressive of a total absence of such a thing as thought, always necessarily vulgar, when one is surrounded by vulgar people. I gave him time to be *natural* that I might be *easy*: and then went upstairs, leaving my assistant and two constables at the foot. Mrs Richardson shewed me in, but the mint was locked, on the principle of the Queen's establishment, where valuables run a risk of being taken away. I knocked and listened. Surely my grandees were in dishabille. At last my appeal, which they knew probably was not a usual one, produced uneasiness, so that the cool-bloodedness, which betokens high breeding was reversed – low words, but quick – rapid movements – small chatterings. At length, perhaps a mere hazard, a voice inquired –

"Is that you, Missus Richardson?"

"No," replied I.

"Mister Richardson?"

"No," again.

"Who, then?"

"A friend."

And so the door gave way to the charmed word.

"Friend? Why, a lie!" said the voice of a man.

"Perhaps not," said I, as I stood before them, and made my usual rapid survey.

I had been wrong in my expectation. The fustian jacket had not taken the place of the surtout, and my ladies were in the same splendid attire I had seen them in on the previous day, only the bonnets were not on their heads – adorned with an exquisite abundance of fine hair, smooth and glossy, and done up in the first style of fashion. Yes, I defy you to have found in Moray Place more personable young women;

nor if I had been there on a visit of condolence for the loss of one of their dearest friends, could I have found manners more staid and correct – I might add graceful, if I could lay claim to knowing much of the true and the false of that accomplishment. But all this I observed by one or two rapid glances diverted from my principal investigation, which latter yielded me at first but little: the indispensable bed, the table and chairs, the plate-rack, and some trunks.

It was clear that they had resolved on no work that day, and no trace of their machinery was visible. My principal hope lay in an inviting press; and as I made a motion to proceed towards it, I thought I observed something like an indication that my gentleman would make free with the door; so applying my fingers to my mouth, I gave a shrill whistle, the sound of which echoed through the flat, startled my ladies out of their composure, and, what I wanted, reached the ear of my assistant, who, obeying the call, was instantly at the door.

I now proceeded to my work of search. From the lower part of the press I drew out the identical fustian coat and trousers described to me by Richardson.

"Your working-suit," said I to Harvey, who seemed to survey the articles with extreme contempt. "A fustian coat," continued I, as I traced the blots of chemicals, and traces of quicksilver, and various scorchings, "is a thing I cannot but treat with respect, when it belongs to arms of independence. It is the fustian that makes the broad-cloth and the silks."

"They're not mine," said Harvey; "they must belong to the house."

"They ain't Mr Harvey's, I assure you, sir," said Miss Matilda Jerome.

"Perhaps not," said I, as I proceeded, "some people have a habit of possessing things that do not belong to them – *possession* just wants a point to make *property* and perhaps this point is awanting here."

Forthwith I produced from the press several likely things – a bottle of quicksilver – some others with chemicals unknown to me – a portable vice with a screw to fix to the table, which latter had the screw mark upon it still – a hammer – files, coarse and fine – the indispensable stamp – but no galvanic battery as I was led to expect, – a circumstance which puzzled me, because I never could suppose that such adepts could be contended with the old process of salt and friction.

I had got enough for my purpose in the meantime, so, turning round –

"Please put on your bonnets and plaids, my ladies," said I, "that you, Mr Harvey, and I, may walk up the High Street to my quarters."

They obeyed with something even like alacrity, on the principle of that sensible man known to history, who, when standing at the gallows foot, said, "If it is to be done, let it be done quickly." Such are the advantages of having to do with genteel people.

I have no doubt we made an excellent appearance in our promenade up the High Street, only I doubt if anyone could comprehend the possibility of such people condescending to enter a police cell. In searching the women we got, strangely enough, no bad money, but a considerable amount of good. The deposit on the window-soles had been intended for this day's work, and scared a little by its having been taken away, they had resolved on outdoor adventures.

I still wanted something, as I have said, to complete the catalogue of my articles in the working department, and, above all, I required to connect Mr Harvey with that, so I applied to him for help.

"I wish to know where you live, when in town, Mr Harvey."

"In Mr Campbell's, Bell's Wynd," he replied promptly affording still the same evidence of the advantages of having to do with high-bred people.

"Then you will please go with me and point it out."

"Certainly."

And getting again my assistant, I proceeded with him to Bell's Wynd, where, having mounted one of the worst stairs in that dark alley, we came to a wretched little dwelling of two rooms and a dark closet. How the great man could have put up in that hovel is difficult to conceive, except upon the supposition that the *swells* shrink when they get home. With the exception of a truckle-bed and a shake-down, there was scarcely a bit of furniture in the house; nor could I find a recess in any way inviting to me except the dark closet, which was adroitly barricaded by the mattress of the shake-down, upon which Mrs Campbell, a miserable invalid, lay in squalid misery. I made short work here. Laying hold of the mattress, I pulled it and its burden away from the closet door into the middle of the floor. A loud scream burst from the invalid, which, from her look I knew to be intended as a fence to the closet, and not an expression of pain. The door was not locked, the bed and its occupant having probably been deemed a sufficient bar.

"Ye've murdered me," cried the cunning wretch, so near her grave, and yet so keen in the concealment of vice. "The malison o' the Lord light on your head, and blast it! Haud awa'! My grave-claes are in that closet, and nae man will enter till that day when my soul gaes hame to glory."

"If you never die till you're *fit* you'll live forever," said I, when I saw there was not a trace of grave-clothes in the dark hole, – from which, however, I brought the galvanic battery, which I had found awanting in Ashley Buildings to complete the apparatus, along with sixteen base shillings. I also got some other things of less importance.

"And now, Mrs Campbell, I will push you back again," said I, as I impelled the mattress to its old place.

"And the devil push *you* hame," she cried, "for you've murdered me."

And she groaned even in that way which aged people do when their wickedness is brought home to them; for that there was a complicity in these old people with Harvey, I had no doubt, even from the conduct of the harridan, – a conclusion confirmed by the assertion of Campbell himself that Harvey was his nephew.

I now took Mr Harvey back to the Police Office, thinking, as I went, upon the small amount of real happiness enjoyed by these adventurers among the rocks that lie in the midst of civilisation. Harvey's domestic comforts may be guessed from the account I have given. He was a man, and could bear the want of ease at night, in consideration of his privilege of walking the streets in a fine dress, and dining in the "Rainbow", with respectable people next box. But what are we to say for the women, with apparently delicate forms, and at least so much of feminine feeling as we might see shining through their really handsome faces? One might sum up all their pleasure in saying, that it consisted in promenading the streets in a silk gown. Even then they cannot be, and are not, devoid of fear. The same fear follows them home to an extinct fire, a truckle-bed with a few thin clothes, into which they huddle themselves, and try in sleep to get away from their own thoughts, – which thoughts sometimes go into the forms of dreams, wherein they take their own way, rejoicing in the tricks of a horrible nightmare. Such a being is everything but the woman she was intended to be, – her enjoyments everything but the affections and sympathies she was made to feel.

Of course, I am assuming here, and I go upon appearances, that Miss Matilda Jerome and Miss Elizabeth Jackson were not originally Arabs. I might make another estimate in that case, for these are seldom touched by fear; and being against society, as society is against them, there is some inversion in them, the true nature of which, in enabling them to seek some strange kind of happiness, we cannot understand, – at least I could never understand it, and I have seen them in all humours. I suspect, however, that what we here sometimes call happiness, is only a kind of accommodation of misery. Thus they take the *sign* for the *thing*; and when they are roaring over the tankard, they think they are enjoying themselves. Perhaps they have more of the real thing in the hardness of their rebellion; for I think I have read somewhere, that man (and woman too, I suspect) is such a strange being that he can feel a pleasure in the very *spite* of pleasure. I can't say I would relish that happiness very much.

Well, I find I am at my old trade of spinning morals, without a touch of which I suspect my experiences would not be of much service to mankind; and if I had had no hope of that, I doubt if I would have been at the trouble of opening my black book of two thousand detections. I have little more to say about my grandees. They were brought to trial before the High Court, where, on the evidence of Richardson and his wife, the urchins who found the pieces, our own testimony, and the tale told by the utensils, they were found guilty. This was not, as I have said, the first, nor the second, nor the third time for the gentleman; but the ladies had never been handled so roughly before. Harvey got eight years' penal servitude, and the two belles five years each. As they sat at the bar, I could not help thinking of their appearance that day I took them for ladies of rank on a mission of charity and mercy. Surely our real LADIES, in their present rage for finery, never think how easily, and by what base copyists, they are imitated.

One word more on this subject. I am certainly not over-fastidious as regards female dress. I have seen it in all its varieties, from the scanty cincture that adorned our first mother Eve, to the ingenious complications of modern taste and refinement; but I must observe, with all proper deference to the ladies, that, in adopting the prevalent redundancy of skirt, the *imitated* have become the *imitators*, as the first of these "circumambient amplitudes" that I ever saw in Edinburgh, was sported by one of the most distinguished "Nightingales" that ever walked Princes Street. In fact, after the experience of thirty years, I find it almost impossible to distinguish the maiden from the matron, – the human vehicle for smuggled or surreptitiously acquired property from the sonsy housekeeper, – or the frail Magdalene, who knows there is a living secret to conceal, from the *robust* "habitante" just returned from an annual visit to her country cousins; nay, Paterfamilias himself, I have heard, on entering a cab or a box at the theatre, has *breathed*, if he did not *utter*, a heartfelt and pocketfelt anathema against such a superabundant and inconvenient display of hoop and crinoline.

Without attempting to quote the words of Pope as to "ribs of whale", I would simply say to all LADIES, as Hamlet said to the players, "I pray you avoid it."

The Whisper

I HAVE OFTEN THOUGHT of the different kinds of outlaw characters which have fallen in my way. If you take the general term "thief", then you can arrange them into sneakers, fighters, bolters, and pleaders. I need not go into a description, where the traits are so evident; but if I were asked to say which of the kinds is the most troublesome, I would fix upon the first. You can overcome a fighter, watch a bolter at the window, replead a pleader, but a sneak, gifted with cunning, who lies, crawls, lurks, winds, and doubles, requires all your wits. To match them all demands many powers both of body and mind, but, beyond all, courage, both moral and physical; and it is not to be wondered at, nor attributed to me as self-praise, if I say that in my experience I have not found many men who combine the gifts. One man has one, another another, and they are useful each in his department, where the character of the criminal is known. That, however, cannot be ascertained till the gentleman has been tested, and the whole tribe flit about so much that they become *new* in the various towns.

David Howie, originally belonging to North Leith, was famous about 1836, chiefly for his escapes by *bolting*; not that he escaped always, for we had him several times through hands, but that he had as yet been successful beyond our wishes, and had a great objection to the other side of the water. We repeatedly were within arm's-length of him, but his recklessness in leaps from windows, his speed, and confidence in these qualities, enabled him to baulk us oftener than any man I have known. Still he stuck to Edinburgh; a strange fatality that in thieves and housebreakers, – their remaining in a town where they not only know that they are known to the officers, but where they have been again and again convicted. However this may be explained, – and I won't attempt it, – it is clear enough that as this knowledge of them increases, they become gradually defiant. They become settled in a trade which they think (and, as our society is formed, they are not far wrong) it is absolutely necessary they should follow; the necessity being, of course, a consequence of their own acts; which necessity again renders it necessary that society should have nothing to do with them.

Howie, unlike many of them, tried other places, – that is, "went to the grouse," – and we thought we were quit of him; but intelligence reached us from Stirling, in the same year, 1836, that he had cleared out a watchmaker's shop there, got the stolen property sent to London, and escaped the fingers of the officers by leaping from a high window, in his old Edinburgh style. A considerable period elapsed. It was known afterwards that he went to London, and got the large quantity of watches and jewelry disposed of. Knowing, as I did, that he must now have been what they call "flush," I expected him to his old haunts. I had experience as well as theory to justify this expectation. A "flush" thief has the same yearning to get back to his native place that a rich Indian has, after he is sure he can overtop his old school fellows. Nor are they without an object; often a great desire to figure among the girls, whose affections are competed for, and earned just as the gentleman has it in his power to gratify them with money. Perhaps, were I permitted to look out of my profession a little, I might say they are not unlike their neighbours in this respect, though I would not take it upon me to say that every man has a side-look to the sex in his efforts to make cash to gratify them when wives.

At least, in Beau Howie's case, I was just as sure that he would have a "fancy" with him, or get one here on his return, as I was satisfied he would turn up in the old dens. Nor was I wrong. "The Bolter" was in due time seen, dressed in the first fashion, so that he would not have shamed "plush" at the clubhouse in Princes Street if he had gone to ask whether His Grace or My Lord was in town; but our David was, in one respect, even more sensible than another of that name, – insomuch, at least, as he did not demean himself so as to earn the ridicule of his "fancy". Nowhere, indeed, can we see the wonderful effect of dress and money working with more effect than in the attraction a "swell" exercises over the lower class of unfortunate females; he is a very god among them;

but David had made his choice of a helpmeet and a worshipper in a woman – Ann McLaren – whom we all knew as "The Hooker," from her art in transferring, – a dark gipsy-looking wench, with eyes that could see to the bottom of a pocket a foot deep, and fingers that could search it for other things than a psalm book; and withal, so far as genius and a pretty face went, quite worthy of so clever a fellow as "The Bolter," and so accomplished a gentleman.

The moment I heard he had taken up with this woman, I considered him secure, for women make a dangerous "trail" to men of this stamp, – not that they betray willingly, which they seldom do, but their activity, and gossiping about their "fancies," and the endless ramifications of their small ways, soon get to our ears. I had only to trace the female to find the male bird; but soon found that she was, as they call it in their slang, alive or awake. One day, I got my eye upon her in the High Street. She had no time for doubling that day, and was bolder, or perhaps off her guard, for no creature can be forever a watcher, – the mind must have a rest; perhaps, too, she was hungry. At any rate, I traced her to a stair in the Grassmarket; but I must wait long enough to be certain it was not merely a house of call. Indeed, from my knowledge of the stair, – and what stair was I not compelled to know? – I was pretty well made up to the conclusion that there she and David passed their sweet lives of innocence and ease.

By inquiries, I was able to fix upon the room they

occupied. There were several windows connected with the lodging, and these required to be looked to. It was a part of the many wonders told of "The Bolter," that, knowing his genius for leaping, he took his lodging accordingly, not on the ground floor, because he might expect an ordinary watch at the window, – nor very high, for then he might break his neck, – but something between, not beyond his hope of getting to the ground, but greatly beyond the notion of a policeman that he would attempt it. I must have him at any chance for the Stirling affair, and required not to be scrupulous. Otherwise I must give up, and wait for a new charge. A little refining on the danger of his not being identified by the Stirling witnesses, – and, after all, he was only suspected, – or of not finding any of the watches, – which I could hardly expect, – would have ruined my enterprise. "The Bolter" was too important a personage to let slip, from my fears of myself being liable to the charge of taking up a man innocent, at least, of any *unpunished* crime.

I selected the hour of midnight, the most auspicious for many reasons, – though, no doubt, often cruel, for while a man is most easily taken in bed, so it is proportionally hard to drag him from the twining, soft arms of love to the encircling grip of unkindly iron; but, then, what right had he to call me and my men from our homes and beds to look after him? I had several officers prepared for an encounter. There were all the windows to guard, because he might leave one room and fly to another. To make sure work, I posted a man at every window, ready to receive David in his bolt, reserving for myself the high privilege of paying my respects to him personally.

All was ready, – a dark and still night, no light at the back of the lodging where the men stood concealed, and scarcely a sound anywhere, except the echo of some tread of a late passenger going along the Grassmarket. I ascended the stair with no more noise in my step than a velvet-footed cat would make in nearing a rat-hole. Got to the landing place, – listened at the door, – no noise. Gone to bed, thinks I, happy in each other's bosoms. Hard fate of mine, to be obliged to part such hearts! but then a comfort it was to part those whom God had not joined, – and then, peradventure, join them again in a honeymoon trip over the sea. It was no fault of mine that their lives had not been lovely. Knocked very gently, – no answer. Again, – no answer, but a whispering. "It is, Davie," I heard Ann say; "get up." Anon came a rumbling noise, the meaning of which I understood, – they were barricading the door. Then with my knowledge of the man, it was for me now to be obstreperous, yea, as noisy as I could. In a *battue* you profit by making as great a kick-up as possible, to get the animals in the safe place. I would either catch him or drive him out of the window into the kindly embrace of my nurses outside. These crazy doors are no impediments; I placed my back to the panels, my foot to the opposite side of the narrow passage, and drove it in with a crash, for the table and chairs behind flew off, adding their confused noise to that of the splintered door. At that instant the window drew up, and all I could see of "The Bolter" was the tail of his shirt as he disappeared from a height of fifteen or twenty feet. Thinking I had not seen the flight, Ann ran to the window, drew it down, and met me, prepared; and I, knowing he was safe, was as much at my ease.

"Where is Howie gone?" said I.

"You are on the wrong scent," said she; "he doesn't live here."

"And whose clothes are these?"

"These! Why, they belong to my husband, who has gone out. If you will wait" – (no doubt to give David time to get off) – "I will tell you all about it. My man's name is —"

"I am not curious, Ann," said I, "about your *husband;* I only want to search the house." This I accordingly did, smiling as I saw "The Hooker" so keen to hook time by even helping me in my search where she knew nothing was to be found. Yes, there was absolutely nothing. The watchmaker's stock had melted away into the usual fluidity in London – a result a little alarming to me, if I had been by nature alarmed, which I am not, for though "The Bolter" was sufficiently habit and repute to justify his being at that moment snug in my nurses' arms, I had yet no charge against him, except the old suspicion of the Stirling affair, – a suspicion merely, – and I stood exposed to the risk of being defeated by a verdict of "not guilty," – always, in such cases as this, as disagreeable to me as agreeable to the panel.

The longer Ann could get me to wait the more light-hearted she got, – waxing merry as the hope rose upon her that she had "done me" by detaining me from the pursuit of her master, lover, and copartner. I was in no hurry to undeceive her, and, moreover, I had no available charge against her. I knew her subtlety too well to try to get anything out of her. So quietly bidding her goodnight, and hoping her husband would soon be in to comfort her for my intrusion, and the smashed door and broken tables and chairs, all of which she passed over without a charge for breakage, I left her. On reaching the foot of the close, I found the shirted David in the embrace of his tender nurses, having been caught in the arms of one of them just as he threw himself from the window. We proceeded to deposit him in his crib, sending back afterwards for his clothes.

Next morning I had a conference with the captain. Information was sent off to Stirling, but he feared we would be defeated, in consequence of nothing being found in the house. I was a little uneasy, and was meditating as to whether I could make sure work by getting some other charge against him. And now occurred one of those extraordinary coincidences which have made my life a romance to myself. I happened to be standing in such a position downstairs – thinking of what I was to do – as rendered it quite possible for me to hear a prisoner speaking to anyone outside in the close; and just at that moment I thought I heard the very low and cautious sounds of two persons conversing. I could gather scarcely anything, but I was satisfied a woman outside was talking to one within the bars. I have already alluded to my sense of hearing from which I have derived so much advantage. Yet withal I could catch but little. I detected the words, "Run and make away with the boots," spoken in a kind of loud hissing whisper. Next instant I saw Ann standing in the close.

Losing no time, I proceeded to the Grassmarket, got into the room easily enough, for the broken door was not yet mended; got hold of *the boots*; and met Ann at the close foot, as she was hurrying, with flushed face, and the keen light of anxiety glancing from her gipsy eyes, to execute the commission.

"I have got them," said I, "and will save you the trouble of carrying them up to your husband, who did not return to you last night."

If the glance which followed had been steel – and it had all the light of steel – I would have detected no more in this world.

On getting to the Office, and searching the books, I ascertained that a pair of boots had the day before been taken from the house of Mr Craig, in Church Lane, leading to Stockbridge. To Mr Craig I went. They were the very boots; and that gentleman described to me how they were taken. They happened to be standing on a table opposite the window, and were abstracted by some one who quietly drew up the sash, and deliberately *let it down again*. With my information thus obtained, I looked in upon Howie.

"I have brought the boots, David, which you asked Ann to go down to the Grassmarket for. What purpose do you intend to turn them to here?"

"What!" he cried, "has the b–tch betrayed me, after having spent all my money upon her?"

"No," replied I, "I knew you were anxious about them, and got before her."

"How, in the devil's name, could you know unless you had got her over?"

"That's my business."

"You're the old man," he said coolly enough, for he had no notion that I could discover their owner; "always in compact with the devil, but you'll not hang me yet."

"I don't want. But where did you get these boots?"

"Try to find out," he growled. "They're paid for anyway; no one could stop me at the shop door."

"*Window,* David, lad."

He knew he was caught, and became as dumb as the boots themselves, – satisfied, I believe, that I was in compact with the devil.

He was thereafter taken to Stirling, that the fiscal might try to connect him with the clearing out of the watchmaker's shop. Meanwhile, – so soon do these "fancies" forget their loves, – Ann got another partner; and here, though not much inclined to notice matters out of my own peculiar line, I cannot help remarking how strangely these outlawed beings carry their ties of love and friendship. They are like the knots of ribbons on women's persons, – very nicely bound themselves, but binding nothing else; and, taken off at night, are pinned on next morning to some other dress. Habit enables them, both men and women, to mix old griefs – for they have griefs – with new joys, and these they have, of a crude kind, too. However true the "fancy" is to her swell, she always contemplates the probable shortness of her obligation, and is quite ready for a new bond when some very ungallant Sheriff or Justiciary Lord severs the existing one. I have known cases where one of these Arab-like creatures has sat in the court and sobbed at the fate of her darling mate, and when he was sentenced to death or banishment hopping away with a new swell from the court, pass perhaps a month or two with him, then to sob for his fate; and so on. There is something affecting about many of them, which would melt very stony hearts. Often interesting, kindly creatures, with bosoms that would have been fountains of love and kindness to husbands and children, if they had been better starred, – and they had no voice in the casting of the form of their fates, – they throw away their devotedness on heartless scoundrels, who make tools of them, and mistresses of them, only to leave them on an instant's notice. But then the very changes reconcile them to a fate they can't escape; and thus there is nothing but unhearty laughter and very hearty tears – love's griefs and love's tears again, love's mirth and love's groans forever. But it does not last long, thanks to the fate that is so cruel to them. A few years is the average of their lives. You would be astonished were I to tell you how they have passed from my watchful eye. Three, or four, or five years, and a new set are on my city beat. They come and go like comets, blazing for a time with wild passions, and then away to make room for others. As for the real *artistes*, one has less sympathy. In place of being kept by men, they keep them – often prostituting themselves for them, robbing for them, suffering for them in a thousand ways, ay, even by imprisonment, and often cast away by the heartless scoundrels to die, or, what is worse, to rot without dying.

In the case of our Ann, I traced her for a year or two, and then heard she had died of disease and want. She, no doubt, had had a foreboding of the fate of "The Bolter," nor was it false. He was sent to Stirling as I have said. The fiscal could not identify him as the robber, and he was sent back to us. The charge for the boots remained. It was urged against him as an old offender, and there being no doubt of his guilt, he got seven years. His fate hung upon a whisper; for if I had not overheard the direction to Ann, to make away with the article, I would not have thought of tracing *their* origin any more than that of the rest of his fashionable clothes – all of which we would have thought he had bought and paid for out of the proceeds of the watches and jewelry, very soon spent, as all the money of such persons is, let it be what it may. Nay, they can't keep it. It burns their hands till it is cast away, and then the hands itch again for the touch.

I believe Howie never knew that the breath of a whisper sent him "over the seas and far awa'."

The Ash-Backet

In the case I am now to give, I have no reason to make fault with my horn-and-hoof friend. I could find none of his ordinary weakness, for he certainly did not only his best, but in a style so adroit, that if he had been the only person in the world he would have had reason to gratify himself with his own blessing – always, of course, framed so as to suit the wish that formed it; but, fortunately, he is not the only person in the world, for he was foiled in even his very best laid scheme, so that Burns might have put him in company with the unfortunate "mice and men", only he had no name to give him beginning with the lip-letter; and then the rhythm would have suffered, as a friend of mine said, knowing I could not discover such learned niceties myself.

A watch was amissing one morning from a house in Picardy Place, in 1834. The story was mysterious. A man called Gardner, a sleazy connexion of the servant's, had been in the kitchen; and when the girl's back was turned he had slipped into the drawing-room, where he had been seen by the lady, who he probably thought was out. She missed a gold watch and running into the kitchen charged the man. He denied. A policeman was got, who searched him, but the article was not found on him. When he was brought up to the lieutenant he was discharged, though an old offender, for the good reason that no man saw him take the watch, nor was the same found on his person. Then the servant was suspected by us, but the lady had such faith in her that she could not join us in our suspicions; and the whole affair was rendered doubtful by the fact that the door had been open during the forenoon while the girl was down to the cellar for coals.

It was altogether, in short, a mess, in which no detective "idea" could be discovered by Genius herself. There were suspicions as evident as millstones looked at through a microscope, – collusion between Gardner and the servant, the hiding of the watch by the latter, and so forth, – but these were rebutted by other considerations. The servant had been there for years with nothing amissing, and people don't fall into the devil's hands all at once with a fling as lovers do; and then the open door was enough itself to let in wind sufficient for the dispelling of these thin clouds of gas smoke.

When in the evening I walked down to Picardy Place, I did not take credit to myself, nor do I do so now, for supposing I could, merely by walking the street and looking at the door, clear up the mystery. I went only because the place had for me the usual charm of places where secret things have been done. It was dark, and about nine o'clock. I was passing from

York Place to Picardy Place, north side, expecting to see nothing thereabouts but those spectres of cinder-women, who, once in the lava streets, have a liking for charred things. After all, they are not very troublesome to us. If they get a silver spoon now and then, and don't give it up, we can't say much: the thing is thrown out, and they are so poor. Strange beings though, with characters never studied, for what interest can there be in a poor creature going about grubbing among ashes, and picking up things you would wonder at? For it must be confessed, that cinders, to give them a gleam of heat at night in the holes they live in, are not the main object. Hopeful souls even in ashes, they expect something to "turn up" out of what others cast away. Yes, I say, they have characters, – they won't steal unless the thing comes half in their way, for they have no courage to enable them to be regular thieves. Then they have almost always been *Vesuviennes*, as they are to the end shrivelled toys of man's heartlessness, and all their anger burned out of them by misery. To ask how they live would be vain, for they don't live, – they only breathe and sigh, on food that is enough for their appetite, which is gone.

I saw them at their work, shadows of creatures going from backet to backet. They never look at you; they don't think they have any right to look at a human being, having renounced the thoughts and feelings of our kind. And few look at them; fewer still give them anything, while sturdier petitioners get shillings and sixpences. But as I was thinking something in this way, I saw a male cinder-wife – excuse the expression; a man went up stealthily to a backet, and bent down, and then left it again. I could not comprehend this anyhow. Why had he not the bag? And without the bag, what could he do with cinders? I suspected he had seen me, for he stood in the middle of the street for a time till I had passed. My curiosity was excited; yet, after all, what more easy than to suppose he intended transporting the backet after turning out the ashes? A bit of humble larceny often enough practised by the lowest class of thieves. I stood at the turn of Broughton Street, and saw him approach the pavement again. This time he was bolder for his great enterprise, for I saw him lift the backet and carry it off towards Leith Walk.

"And not turned out the cinders," muttered I, as I came up to the spot where the utensil had lain.

Small things strike more sharply at times than big. I must see. He will empty it on the middle of the street. No, he doesn't; he carries it on and on. He didn't intend to empty it, and I might be left in rather a curious mystery.

"Well, my lad," I said on getting up to him, opposite the end of the north side of Picardy Place, "what are you to do with the backet?"

The old answer –

"What's that to you?"

An answer which, if he had recognised me, as he didn't, he would not have ventured, though I knew him. He had been six times through my hands, but I shied his looks, and kept my hat well down.

"I want to know what you intend doing with the backet?"

"The backet?"

"Ay, the backet."

"It's my own."

"No, I saw you lift it."

"I'm going to empty it."

"Why?"

No answer.

"Then, Gardner," said I, looking at him, "why *don't* you empty it?"

"And so I do," he said, as he heard his name; and suiting the action, not only to the word, but the fear, he threw it down, and way for off.

"No, my old friend," said I, as I seized him; "not so fast, or there will be a greater *dust*."

As I held him, I cast my eye, not without an "idea", upon the ashes. There was something else there than charred coal. I stooped, still holding on by my man, and picked up a gold watch.

"How was I to know that was there?" said he, with an air of triumph.

"Because you put it there in the morning, when you were in Miss ——'s house, under the fear of a search."

"It's a lie, and a foolish one; how could I know that it would be allowed to remain?"

"Easily answered," said I; "but it is not my intention at present to satisfy your curiosity. Take up the backet and come with me."

In the meantime, up comes the servant, crying out if anyone had seen a man with a backet.

"Yes," said I, "here is the man and the backet too."

"You, Gardner!" said the girl, "What, in the name of wonder, do you want with my backet?"

"It was not the backet he wanted," said I, "but this watch which your mistress missed in the morning."

The girl's head ran round as she looked at the man and me, and the backet and the dust.

"Good heavens!" she cried, "I will be blamed and ruined. It will be said I put it there that he, who is my cousin – oh that I ever knew him! – might find it when I put out my ashes at night."

"Never you fear," said I, for I saw by the girl's unfeigned surprise that she was innocent. "The whole story is clear enough."

"Ay, to you and to me," said she; "but how will I get my mistress to see it? Yes, the backet was in the kitchen, and when the policeman came it must have been put there by Gardner."

"All too clear to need so much talk," said I.

"Oh!" cried the terrified girl, "but will you come with me now, and satisfy her?"

"No; I must take this precious cousin of yours to the Office, backet and watch and all, and you will be called upon in the morning; meanwhile, go home and tell your mistress that McLevy requested you to say that he thinks you innocent. If the lady has a spark of sense, she will see it all herself."

But still she wept pitifully.

"Ah, sir, our family have been ruined by this blackguard; my father fed him and cled him, and he has been a disgrace to us all through life; and now, at last, he would be the means of making me suspected of robbing the best of mistresses."

All the while, the hardened scoundrel looked as unmoved as the piece of wood which he used as the means of his villainy.

"Dry up your tears, my good girl," said I; "he'll never trouble you again, take my word for it."

And still blubbering, so that the passers-by began to stand and inquire, she hung by me, imploring me to go with her and satisfy her mistress. It was with some difficulty I shook her off, but at length I succeeded; and as I proceeded upwards, I still heard her sobbing among the crowd. Gardner was silent – perfectly unaffected at the misery into which he had brought his relation. He was safely provided for.

In the morning I went to Picardy Place. The girl opened the door, with a look so thankful, as if she considered me her preserver.

"Have you told your mistress?"

"Oh, sir, I couldn't. I have not slept a wink all night."

"Not told her, foolish girl!" said I.

"No; but you will, and then she will believe."

"Of course she will, and she will be better satisfied when she hears, as I hope she will by and by, that Gardner gets a passage over the seas."

The girl ran quicker than she ever did along that lobby before, opened the door, then shut it behind me, – to watch and listen, no doubt; and who could blame her?

In a few words I explained the whole story to Miss ——, a sharp and benevolent woman; she saw through the trick in a moment.

"But your poor servant is in a terrible state about it, lest you should suspect she had any hand in it."

Without saying a word, she went to the door, –

"Mary," she called, with a loud voice.

No answer; Mary was caught; she was standing up by the wall, so that her mistress could not see her.

"Mary," louder still.

"Yes, m'em," said a voice at her very side.

"Stupid girl, come in here;" and she took the timid creature by the hand, and dragged her in.

"What are you afraid of?"

Whimpering and sobbing.

"Give up; I have no fault to find with you."

"Oh, but you have been so kind a mistress," she said, in a choking kind of way, "that I could not bear – no – I could not bear – bear the very thought that you should suspect me."

And then came another burst.

"Girl, have I not told you that I am satisfied with Mr McLevy's explanation, and that you are no more guilty of taking my watch than Mr McLevy himself?"

"God bless you, m'em, and God bless you, sir, and now I'm happy."

And happy she ran away, relieved of a night-mare which had been upon her throbbing bosom all night, and, not contented with its night work, had clung to her all the morning.

"Ah, this accounts," said her mistress, "for the miserable look she has borne since ever she rose; but that girl will be dearer to me than ever."

That same day Miss ———— and Mary came up and were examined. There was no doubt of Gardner's guilt, yet it was viewed as a strange case, altogether without precedent. The magistrate said that "there really was no substantial evidence against the man upon which he could be charged for stealing the watch. It was altogether circumstantial; no doubt he did it, but no one saw him put the watch in the receptacle where it was found, nor was the watch actually, in a proper sense, found upon him. He might say that if he wanted to find the article, he could have rummaged the backet, – a far more likely act than running away with a load of dust. Indeed, it is not easy to see why he should have followed a course which was so likely to bring upon him the very people on the pavement. It is clear, however, that he may be charged with stealing the backet itself, and, if you please, the cinders; and, as I am told he has been convicted before, the issue will be the same.

It is proper for me to add, for the sake of the girl, that, in my opinion, she is perfectly innocent. It is impossible to bring home to her even a suspicion; for even, on the supposition of concert, how could she know that the ashes and the watch would not be tossed into the cart before her cousin came to take it away?

Then she was not on the stair watching the result of a scheme; she came down only after the article was taken away, and finding it gone, ran after the thief, not even knowing it was Gardner that took it."

Good news for poor Mary, and, perhaps, better afterwards, when her never-do-well relative was transported for seven years, just for stealing a backet. He was obliged to swallow the shell and throw out the kernel.

In this case, vice did not shew her usual weakness. Everything was adroitly played, with the single exception, perhaps, of his running away with what he might have searched; but then he did search, and it was only when he heard the cart that he gave way to what appeared to him to be a necessity. Is not all vice a necessity? If it weren't, I fear I would have skeely for breakfast.

The Blood-Stained Moleskin

MISS BALLENY, a maiden lady with considerable means, and advanced in years, occupied a first flat, with front door, and an area flat beneath, in Buccleuch Place. From some peculiar choice, it would seem, and not from necessity, she kept no regular servant, employing a woman to come occasionally, and do any duties she could not herself perform; nor is it thought she had any extreme penuriousness in her nature, that led to this choice; rather, it would seem that she preferred being alone, having discovered perhaps that the Edinburgh servants are not remarkable for either fidelity or affection towards their employers. It is certain, at least, she was an inoffensive lady, and in many respects amiable and kindly in her feelings.

One night, in February 1845, she was preparing to retire to rest, it being near ten o'clock, – seriously disposed, she had been reading her Bible, and engaged in those thoughts that become one of her years. It has often been remarked, as a strange fact in the economy of nature, that the nearer to a catastrophe, the further the thoughts from it – a kind of security into which we are lulled by a false quietude, betokening a continuance of that peace which we could have wished to be unbroken, and which at least might be expected by those who desire to be in friendship with all men. She was startled in the midst of her lonely musings by a noise, as if someone was endeavouring to force an entry through one of the windows of the lower or area flat. Greatly fluttered, she groped her way to the lobby, which ran from the front area-door to the back, and before she got halfway along it, she encountered a man. Giving a suppressed choking scream, she retreated towards the kitchen, where, being followed by the man, he seized a heavy poker, and struck her a terrible blow on the head.

This, with all its severity, had not it would seem deprived her of sense, for she had set forth such a yell of agony, that it was heard by some of the neighbours. I have heard it said that the intention to kill is rather confirmed and made furious by a thrilling cry – a species of resistance which, expressing horror, is felt by a murderer as an impeachment of his cruelty, besides rousing his fears of being detected; and it is thought that the cruel man was thus roused, for he laid on blow after blow, till the head of his victim bore cuts to the bone as the bloody traces of the terrible onslaught.

A single minute or two sufficed for the work – the woman was bathed with blood, and the hand was again raised to put a certain end to life, when an alarm was raised by the neighbours. The poker was instantly dropped, and the murderer, flying along the dark passage, tried the door to the back; it was locked, and he escaped by the window just as the neighbours were at his heels. He got off, but not without being so far noticed, that they could speak to his general appearance and dress.

Immediately afterwards, doctors were called, the interest displayed by the sympathisers excluding for a time all efforts at tracing the man. So far as was thought, he had made a clean escape, for the indistinct notice got of him could not have amounted to identification, and the lady, almost at the point of death, could not be questioned, nor, as the attack took place when there was scarcely a glimmer of light, could it be expected she would be able to add much to the vague notice of those who saw him escape. I was at the house next day, but it was four or five days after before I could be permitted to question her; and even then, I found it possible to get only some marks which could not afford me much aid. I ascertained, however, partly from her own lips, in broken accents, and partly from the neighbours, just as much as satisfied me, that the man was a young follow about eighteen or twenty, and that he wore a lightish moleskin jacket and trousers. Nothing could be more indefinite, as the dress is that worn by thousands of working men, and the age amounted to nothing.

Next day I was in the High Street, not knowing well how to turn, for where, in the wide expanse of the old town, filled with so many dens, and those often crammed with people of all kinds, was I to find the owner of *the* moleskin jacket and trousers? There were hundreds around me dressed in this common garb: he might as well be among these as in a house, for being certain he was not seen, he would not think it necessary to skulk; and then he had taken nothing with him by which the crime could be brought home to him.

The allusions I have made to chance may tire readers, as well as lay my narratives open to suspicion; yet certain it is, that at that minute, when my eyes were busy surveying the crowded street, my attention was suddenly arrested by one I knew to be a thief, and who wore a moleskin jacket and trousers.

I immediately walked after him, and it struck me that his dress looked like as if it had been washed and dried very recently. This made me curious; and as he walked on, I quickened my steps till I came nearer him, so as to have a better view of his jacket. I thought I could perceive blotches here and there, very like as if marks of blood had been ineffectually attempted to be washed out. I became at length so satisfied, that I stopped him.

"George," said I, for I knew him of old, "you have got your jacket newly washed; but, oh, man, it's not well done."

"What do you mean?" said he.

"Why," said I, "you have forgotten to rub out the stains of Miss Balleny's blood."

In an instant every trace of blood was absent from his cheek, however it stuck to his moleskin – yes, he was instantly pale, and struck dumb.

"Come," said I, "I wish to examine those marks

better, and I would rather make the investigation in the Office."

I accordingly took him there, in the midst of all the ordinary protestations and threatenings, and soon got my suspicions confirmed by the opinions of others. As soon as Miss Balleny was supposed to be able to stand the look of him, he was taken to her bedside. I shall never forget the look of that lady, as she brought her nervous eye to bear upon the man who was supposed to be he who did all that bloody work upon her. A shiver seemed to run over her whole body, as if the sight had brought back to her the terrible feelings of that lone and dark hour.

It seemed that there had been some glimmer, either from the kitchen fire or from the street lamp through the window, I forget which, but there had been enough to enable her to distinguish his dress and general appearance; for, after gazing at him for a time, she said, "O God, that is the very man!" We afterwards got some of the neighbours to add something like identification, and we thought we had enough, with the bloodstains, to authorise a conviction.

The Crown officer having got all the evidence that was to be had, George Kerr was brought to trial before the High Court for the attempt to murder and the housebreaking. Miss Balleny was put into the box as the principal witness; but it became soon apparent that the poor lady had suffered too much to permit of the continuance of that recollection which had served on occasion of the prior meeting. Her mind was gone.

At one time she was positive, at another only suspicious, at another doubtful, only to be more positive again, as the changing thought flickered through her brain. The other witnesses were decided enough as to the dress and generalities; and the washed blood-stains were as decidedly spoken to as marks of such a kind could be; but the fatality lay in Miss Balleny's incapacity; and the jury, after a discriminative charge, brought in a verdict of "not guilty".

All my efforts had thus gone for nothing; but my pride of detection was hurt, and I felt much inclination to stick by my man. I accordingly ascertained that he had gone by the boat to Stirling; and though he had thus left my bounds, he did not take with him my desire to look after his welfare. Nor was it long before my kind demon helped me in my solicitude, for a day or two afterwards the Stirling authorities sent us information that the shop of a Mr Meek had been broken into, on *that* very evening Kerr had left Edinburgh, by a young man answering to his description, and a sum of money, as well as a silver watch, had been abstracted as booty.

It was now my duty to watch again for my man, though I had small hope he would return so soon to town; nor did he. He had gone direct to Glasgow, with the view of getting the silver watch disposed of at a pawn shop. There he was signally unfortunate, for the Stirling authorities had sent a description of the watch and the man to the Glasgow police, who had spread the intelligence among the pawnbrokers. Accordingly, when Kerr offered the article at a pawn shop there, the man to whom it was presented declared immediately that it was stolen, and, sliding between Kerr and the door, endeavoured to detain him. The effort was vain. Kerr darted past him, and outran his pursuers.

Of all this we got timely knowledge, and now I had another chance. Always keeping the moth-instinct in view, I suspected that he would be back to his old haunts; and in this case I was made more than usually hopeful, in counting that the money taken at Stirling must have been spent, and the want of wings to fly further would send him crawling to his old nest. My former inquiries had enabled me to know that his mother lived in Macdowall Street. Thither I went, and somehow or other I felt a kind of certainty that I would find him. I knocked at the door with much confidence, and perhaps, on that account, with much humility and gentleness. Mrs Kerr herself answered, and I remember the conversation –

"Well, Mrs Kerr, have you anyone living with you?" asked I.

"Nobody, sir."

"Quite sure?"

"Perfectly sure. I'm a lone woman, and after what has befallen my poor innocent son, I am very miserable."

"And so you may well be," said I, "for that was a terrible business; but have you no notion where George is?"

"No, no. I have never seen him since that day of the trial; and I fancy the poor fellow is so ashamed of having been suspected of murder that he'll never shew his face in Scotland again."

"And have you no lodgers?" I inquired.

"Not a living soul, sir."

"Well," said I, "I'll just step in and see."

"You are very welcome," she answered, just in that involuntary way that has told me a hundred times that there is somebody in some place where there is nobody; and so we often need to act against the rule that a person cannot be in two places at the same time.

And passing her, I looked round the place she used as a kitchen. No concealing place there. I then opened the other room, and saw nobody; nor did I expect, as she had time enough before answering my knock to make any convenient arrangements.

"Here is a closet," said I.

"No, sir; just a cupboard for odds and ends."

"Locked," said I. "Do you usually lock up your cups and saucers?"

"What I use are in the kitchen," she replied, getting, as I saw, alarmed.

"And have you not got the key?"

"No, it is lost."

Ah! the old story, I thought.

"Well, if it is lost," said I, quietly, "it is the more necessary that search should be made for it. You go and get it *where* it was lost."

"How could it be lost if I knew where it is?" said she, thinking me serious, no doubt.

"Why, that is just a curious part of the case," said I; "and another is, that if you don't go and get it where it was lost, I will get an axe in the kitchen and break open the door."

"What? Do you think my son is there?" said she, in affected wonder.

"Yes," said I. "I think his shame has gone off, and he has faced Scotland again. Get me the key, quick, or —" and I made for the kitchen.

"There," said she, as she drew it out of her pocket; "the Lord's will be done."

And there, upon opening the door, was that blood-thirsty man who had so ruthlessly smashed the head of the aged lady, who never did him a trace of injury, standing bolt upright in a narrow cupboard, which scarcely permitted him to move.

"Ah! once more, George," said I.

The fellow absolutely ground his teeth against each other till I heard the very rasping; a scowl sat on his low brow, so demonic that if I had not been accustomed to such looks it might have made me recoil; and I believe if he had had Miss Balleny's poker, or any other poker, he would have tried his skill at laying open heads on my cranium. But for all these indications the cure is unshrinking firmness; and sure I am, if I had shewn a trace of weakness, he would have fallen upon me on the instant like a tiger.

"There is no use for these looks with me," said I; "you know me of old; so take the cuffs kindly, or worse will befall you."

"But, sir," cried the mother, when she saw her son bound, "is this never to be ended? Has George not been tried and found innocent?"

"Yes," said I. "But we are informed that he robbed a shop in Stirling that very night after he was released; so you see the trial did not shame him quite so much as you thought."

"It's a d———d lie!" burst out the fellow; "I have never been out of Edinburgh."

"To that I can swear," said the parent; for, although she had said, "The Lord's will be done," the mother came back again to lie for her murderous boy. No, no; there is no appeasing of this yearning. I have seen it working in all forms. Even if she had seen those hashes in the head of the poor lady, and the body drenched in blood, drawn by the hand of her son, she could not have stayed that yearning. The moment's horror would have been succeeded by a tear for the victim and a flood for the murderer. So true what someone said to me once – the mother's heart is the sanctuary that shuts out all detectives. It even makes sinners of good people, just as if, being the very stuff the nerve is made of, it kicks heels-over-head all the virtues, which are only phantom things flickering about in the brain.

I confess here to a weakness. When I was taking my man up to the Office, I thought all the world was looking at me. Why so? Since ever that day I saw the mangled head of that poor lady, the vision had haunted me like a ghost, and, having failed in getting the murderer convicted, the spectre followed me more and more, as if insisting I should bring him still to justice; so when I walked him up, I thought, It is done now – I have got him, and, though he won't be hanged, he will be better than hanged, for he must get on the chain and the horrible clogs, and pull his legs after him in Norfolk Island, under a scorching sun, and then he will not be obliged to *draw* the bloody head after him, for it will follow of its own accord, and every gash will make gobs at him.

So we think, and yet I have my doubts whether a man who *could* bring a heavy poker down with all his strength on the head of an unoffending female – I take the one peculiar case – is capable of relentance. The softness is not in him. I do not say that God is not able to bring it, but I do say that where such a change comes it must be a miracle.

We next sent intelligence to Stirling that the now famous George Kerr was safe in our hands. Meantime we knew that the Glasgow police had sent on the watch there, so that the watch and the watch-stealer would meet opportunely, where Mr Meek could speak both to the one and the other. It soon got known to the Crown agent who it was that had broken into Mr Meek's shop, and I do not doubt that this knowledge helped to quicken the Stirling fiscal's wits in making a clearer case of the robbery than the Edinburgh official had been able to do. The trial was fixed for the next Circuit. Every effort was made, witnesses called from Glasgow, and all those ferreted out in Stirling that could say a single word to help so good a cause as bringing so cruel a man to justice. If it had been some years earlier, he might have been tried for his life as a housebreaker; but as it was, it turned out as well as could be expected. He was sentenced to ten years' transportation.

No case ever gave me more satisfaction than this. The people of Edinburgh had been disappointed by the issue of the former trial, and when it was known that he had been sentenced to transportation for a robbery committed on the day of his liberation, the satisfaction was great, and all the greater that the robbery made sure of the real heartless, incurable character of the villain. Indeed, it is not too much to say that the act was worse than murder, for the lady was so desperately maimed that her recovery, with ruined intellect, was rather an additional evil to that first inflicted.

The Belfast Key

I HAVE NEVER been able to ascertain where all those images of people go to in my mind. I am sure they are not packed up, each with its little film of card away back, the last got being always nearest the eye, like a barrel of herring on its side; for in that case I could not get out some fifteen-year-old one, as I do so easily, to confront it with some of my children, who have been away round the world and come back again. Nay, the older they are the brighter they are and then they don't trouble me any more than if they were dead – like the flies in Dr Franklin's bottle of Madeira, I have read of somewhere, – and are always brought alive again just when they're wanted. Neither do they trouble me, as they certainly do others, who have what they call a fancy, where the little things are eternally getting restive, rising up and flapping their wings, and flying hither and thither in confusion, bothering the soul, so that it becomes terrified at midnight with ghosts and phantoms, and producing hysterics, and Heaven knows what more. I have no fancy. If I had had, I would have been dead long ago; for how could I have borne such a host of thievish and murdering-looking likenesses of banished or hanged men, rising up on me in myriad, and haunting me everywhere, as if I had banished or hanged them in spite of the innocence they all protest, and sometimes look so much like? No! Thank Heaven, I sleep, and have always slept, not like a top with its unobserved whirl, but like a log. And if I should be wakened, to catch some Bill Brash who has taken it into his head to come back from Norfolk Island, whither I had sent him, I find the image of Bill as ready at my call as if it had been fluttering and tormenting me all these seven years.

It is now a pretty old story, that of the lifting of two piles of valuable tweeds – worth a hundred guineas – from the door of Mr Young's shop in the High Street. I got notice almost on the instant, and listening down, saw how the affair had been managed. The glass door inside had been shut, and the piles had lain on either side of the space between the outer door and the inner. The affair looked curious. The piles were four feet high, and every web rolled on a pretty heavy piece of wood, so that it would have been a considerably tough job to have *snatched* even one and made off with it in the very heart of a passing multitude. The shopmen hail, of course, their theory, as all people in such circumstances have. There must have been, they thought, at least half a dozen about it, each taking a piece and running off with it, just as ants do their bags when they want to get them out of the sun. I knew better; such a scene would have been noticed outside, because the very *succession* of the liftings would have taken greatly more time than the pauses of passengers could have permitted. In short, I saw that one person could do it better than a dozen, taking quietly, after a survey, first one web and then another, depositing in succession, and coming and going. Then there was the inevitable conclusion that the webs were not far off – a great point; but the webs *were* deposited, and would be where they were; so my case was not one of chase, and Time to be taken by the forelock.

Nor was I long in getting my theory confirmed. Just as I was inquiring up and down for a hint, I met a woman who said she had seen a young man turning the corner of Borthwick's Close, with a piece of cloth under his arm.

"One piece?" said I.

"Ay, ane," replied she, a little groggy; "and plenty, for, my faith, he was staggering wi' the weight."

"Do you know where he got it?"

"No, but he looked as if he had come up the street, and what was I to think but just that he was a snip! And then they aye walk quick, the snips, they're so glad to get on their feet."

"They don't stagger, though," said I.

"Sometimes on 'little Sunday,' – that's Monday, – for they're aye a day or twa ahint the other workmen in their weekly jubilees."

I listened patiently, for I never repress witty witnesses; their conceit makes them say more than your grave informants, who have no tickling inside their clay heads.

"Did you see enough of him to enable you to speak to his appearance?" I inquired again.

"Only the hinder-end," said she, with a groggy smirk, "which is aye big in them. I could swear to the hinder-end o' a snip, but no to a particular ane, for they're a' alike, the swivel, too, that maks them rock sae when they're in a hurry, is a' o' a piece; and then, they aye snuff with the right nostril, which they haud to a side, to save what they're sewing."

And so on she would have gone, – for, as I have said, she had had a dram, – but I had got all she could tell, and, inquiring her name, I got on with my thoughts. Could it, after all, be possible that this bold fellow had returned and returned to the treasury, and picked off twenty bales of goods all one-by-one? The man that achieved this was worthy of my acquaintance-ship, and even this consideration alone would have inspired me to a capture, but then, such an artist could scarcely have been unknown to me, unless he were a new importation, and that was unlikely, for he must have arranged his resetting place, and have known the closes.

On what I had got, my theory was formed. Going down to Hunter's Square, I went south by Blair Street, till I came to the Cowgate, and then along to the foot of Borthwick's Close; I then stepped into a grocer's shop, – always the historical register office of the neighbours, who can't do without their penny candle, red herring, and ounce of tea.

"Any strangers about the close, Mr Heron?" said I.

"I believe the turner's son has come home," he replied.

"You mean by the turner, the old man whose shop is there, but who lives elsewhere?"

"Just so."

"But Brash can't live in the shop?" I rejoined.

"Not sure, the father is weakly, and has not been working for some time."

"And perhaps the son may sleep among the sawdust?"

"Not unlikely. I'm sure, at least, he hangs about here, for I saw him lig-laggering wi' the women opposite my window yesterday."

"But he has never bought any cheese, or herring, or bread, or a candle, and taken it away as if to use them somewhere here about?"

"Yes; he bought bread and herring yesterday, – no candle, – and he went up the close with them."

"If he had been living with his father, he wouldn't have come here."

"No; the family were never customers of mine."

So far well enough. There was someone in that close, who, if *my* memory served me, was very well able, from *experience*, to do the bold and clever thing that had been done; but it was no business of mine to be seen thereabout just at the time when I wanted somebody, and when some other body might say to another body that McLevy was there, for the people had grit into their heads that I could be nowhere but where I should be, I would rather, at that juncture – it was now getting late – be among the light-o'-loves. Really, in these very squeamish days I know not how to get rid of my old vocabulary; we used to have good, sturdy names for a certain class, – not those of Mohammed's paradise, with the black eyes they have at their heavenly birth, but those who have black eyes of another kind, generally given by one to another, and not just so productive of love. So I have been careful in avoiding slang, – a kind of language rather beneath me, – but then, certain names are useful, if not necessary. Were I a scholar, I might coin an appellation for them – not a reproachful one, perhaps; for vicious and immoral as they are, alas, who can tell the insidious temptations that were employed to render them the fallen guilty beings they have now become, – outcasts possibly from a comfortable home, to become the criminal creatures you now behold?

Under whatever name you like, I was accordingly soon there, with a notion, not at all unjustified, that my tweed-lifter – like other people who have done a great feat and made a fortune – would, in place of going home and snoring out his triumph, go where "pleasure waits him" were it for no other purpose than just to give his relieved heart some play, or get some recompense for his trouble. And who that by his own hands had made £100 in half an hour, upon a capital of a bad shilling, would not feel happy, and inclined to be among merry people, like these black or blue-eyed damsels, always jovial, even in the very midst of their wretchedness and tears, – not tears of joy, pure and unmixed, as they were wont to be in their days of innocence, and before this moral blight had fallen upon them.

I was thus naturally led to Hyndford's Close, – a very good specimen of a rut in a dried stream of lava, which, I fancy, is just a kind of cinders. I went through several *establishments*; and last came to the great one, with nine or ten beds, if you can call by that name the four fir-posts, with the lath bottoms, and the pieces of yellow cotton sheets, and scarcely less yellow blankets, and strips of old carpets or horsecloths spread over them, and the pillows, – little bags, sometimes filled with teased oakum, among which I have often found jewels and gold watches. In that house I once discovered, as sharp a trick as ever I played, if it was not sharper than the discovery. I had traced a £20 watch to the pocket of "The Crow," and there lost it just as she was supping her sheep's-head broth out of a capacious bowl, with what they call a horn cutty. I searched about everywhere and could not find the watch, yet I was certain it was in that room. I had almost given up, when I noticed her very slow with her kail. I knew it wasn't fear prevented her satisfying her appetite, for "The Crow" feared me no more than she did her mother, whom she was in the habit of thrashing, because, as she said, the old woman had taught her her trade. There must be some secret under this sudden want of appetite.

The kail would not go down in the bowl, because she would not put them down into her stomach. I suddenly caught a thought. "Let me taste your kail, Bess," and my first sup was of the watch, which she had slipped into the bowl when she saw me enter. When she took flight to the South Sea, I would have taken a year from her banishment for her magpie trick, Crow as she was.

I need not say how vain it is to question these queens of Rougedom – another modern name – as to any gentlemen of the light-fingered tribe being among their subjects, – unless you are to go direct contrary to their contraries, – nor with what confidence they lie in your face as they hold up their queenly counte-nances. They are all of a piece, these queens, and a strange piece indeed. You may know every section by mark, – the purple face, always with a rotten-like tumefaction about it, set on the thick hull neck, which again is placed on the untidy bosom – beneath which a heart throbs, rankling with bitter feelings against society, whose laws have excommunicated them from its pale, – all surmounted with the sleazy mutch, set off with a crop of faded French flowers, collected from her subjects. And there is pride in this corporation, as she looks big, talking of "*my* house," sometimes, at least once in my experience, "*my* establishment," "*my* young ladies," sometimes these one day without a shoe, and the next (a pawn redemption day) decked out with articles every one of which has its eventful history; how it belonged to some fine lady in Moray Place, – how it came down to the lady's maid, – how it ran the gauntlet of passing turn about among the household, with a dogging envy of its possessor for the hour, – how it had charmed a "colley" from George Square to Hyndford's Close, where he lost his watch, – how it has been pawned a hundred times, and yet retained its power of drawing.

Even with so proud a dame I seldom did more than give her a nod, as I opened the door and took my walk, as I did now among the beds and cells. I searched everywhere, – all the working bees out among "the flowers of Edinburgh" to bring home the *honey* in the shape of *money*, – but there was, far ben, with a window looking into a ruinous area to the east, a room I remember very well, and the door of which I had passed. I returned to enter, but found it shut, and locked inside. These crazy hindrances I have often made short work of, by putting my back to them, in obedience to which they generally fly open, with the advantage of anticipating the preparation the inmates honour me with. I applied that force-key now, for I knew that any suspected denizen of that inside heaven would rather jump the window for the opposite place than welcome me to his bower of bliss. A gas burner was flaring away right in tin; faces of three persons, two women and a man. I saw nothing, of course, but the three faces, with the six eyes looking clear, but in nowise bewildered with anything like consternation, only the man did not seem easy in a position which, judging from the apparent cosiness, he might have thought enviable by some whose tastes lie in that heavenward direction.

"You seem to be very comfortable, my friend," said I, "I am sorry to flutter your wings in that paradise."

A growl repaid a handsome compliment; but such is the way of the angels in these paradises. "I will thank you to get up," said I, "Don't, Jim; he has no right," said the guardian angel on the left.

"Ay," said the other on the right, "what right have you to disturb decent people in their own apartments?"

"Come, I say; get up; don't you see I'm waiting?"

"Shan't," growled the man; "you've no charge against me. I came to Edinburgh only yesterday."

"Where from?"

"Belfast."

"What street?"

"Huntly Street."

"No such street there, I suspect," said I. "Come, get up, and dress, and the ladies can cover their faces with their hands."

"Won't do, Bill," whispered the left one; "it's McLevy, if anything's wrong, it's all up."

"So you won't rise?" I persisted.

"What for?" roared the swain, getting at once into a rage, as he probably contrasted our cells with his present angel-guarded position.

"Just to don your clothes," said I; "I want to know if, by searching, you can find anything in the pockets which I may think curious in the arts; but I have some delicacy in rifling pockets. There may be money in them, and you might charge me with a deficit. Come."

"I never rifled pockets anyhow," said he, as he fixed

his eyes on me, with a look that did not change my conviction that I had had his image for a good many years in my mind, associated with the honours offered to him by a judge, and a jury, and a full court, before he sailed for Norfolk Island.

Yes, even though thus translated, with the light of his sister angels shining on him, I knew him the moment I threw my eyes over him.

"Well," he cried at length, as he started, and stood before me, yet, I thought, under the belief that I did not recognise him.

"Quick and cover; here's your breeches. I will be your footman; here's the vest, and next the coat, stockings, neckcloth, boots," – all in succession, with proper intervals. "All right; now you are in a position to appear before the ladies."

"What next?" said he, sneeringly.

"Ripe, and tell me what is in your pockets."

"There's a handkerchief," said he, pulling out, "a penknife, a quid of tobacco, a pipe, a bit cheese, an empty phial, -- that's all. Does any one of them belong to *you?*"

"Nothing more?" said I, "Try again. I thought I heard the phial strike against a bit of steel, perhaps a key. Come, out with it; I am curious in keys."

But he wouldn't.

"I'll help you, my good fellow," said I; "you know I'm your flunkey."

And plunging my hand into the right outside pocket of his coat, I brought out a good-sized outer door key.

"Where's the door that key opens?" asked I.

"In Belfast."

"Belfast again, and in Huntly Street! No doubt the house will have a number too – 10,060?"

"Number eleven."

"Well, we shall go there tonight," said I. "Are you ready?"

And not waiting for a reply I took him gently by the arm, and moved him out. The inevitable all-up was now in the ascendancy, and he went like a lamb till we got to the High Street, where I gave him in charge to my assistant, there waiting. I had the key in my hand; and, coming to Borthwick's Close, "This way," said I; "I have a call to make before setting out for Belfast."

Nor did I take any notice of the change that, like a flash, came over his countenance. He was a ruddy, healthy fellow, new from a voyage, and had not yet taken on the close-colour, but he was in an instant pale enough to satisfy even Despair herself. Proceeding down the close, my man and assistant before me, we came to the turner's shop.

"I want to go in here," said I.

"I have nothing to do with that place," said he, "This is not Huntly Street, Belfast."

"No, nor number eleven; but just you open the door," (handing him the key,) "and let me in."

Though the key seemed to burn his fingers, he was yet so satisfied of the all-up necessity, that he seemed to grasp it nervously, and proceeded with his own hand to open the door.

It was much too dark to see into the hole, but there was light in an opposite window; and getting, upon a rap, the end of a halfpenny candle, I came over.

"I want to see," said I, "whether this turning lathe turns out any tweeds."

And straightway our eyes beheld all the webs of Mr Young's two piles of cloth, built neatly up against the wall. I counted them carefully, for I had a pride in the exact number – thirty pieces, all there, not one wanting.

"You can identify these, Mr William Brash," said I, looking my prisoner directly in the face, "as the webs of cloth you stole from Mr Young's shop door some four hours ago?"

"Brash is not my name."

"Not now, but it was before you went on your travels; for which jaunt you were indebted to me, I rather think."

His courage couldn't stand my last appeal, and he seemed as well satisfied that I could do no more for him as anyone with a cancer could be with the doctor who administered a hemlock poultice, which could nip, but never heal.

Having taken him to the Office, and provided for him carefully, as a valuable addition to our stock of moral curiosities, I got the thirty bales up, which were all safely delivered to Mr Young; but that gentleman, I rather think, had no less difficulty in accounting for the seizure, so near his premises, than in understanding how these thirty heavy pieces could have been carried away, in so short a time, by one man. That there were no assistants, was admitted by Brash himself, who was sent abroad for the second time in ten years.

The Handcuffs

IN THE YEAR 1836, which was in Mr Stewart's time, information came to the Office from the quiet town of Peebles, – so quiet, that Lord Cockburn says, in some of his books, "if you want to make a public proclamation anywhere so as not to be heard, go to Peebles, and it is buried for ever," – that the house of a gentleman there had been robbed on a Wednesday night, and a number of articles, among which were a new greatcoat and a pair of Wellington boots, had been carried off. However deaf Peebles may be to a proclamation, it certainly – at least among the high authorities there – cannot be charged with insensibility to the breach of the laws, for a capital account it was which we got, embracing all the particulars, the articles carried off, and the description of a person, once a servant in the family, who was suspected of the breaking-in and the abstraction. There was only one want – not a hint of the direction the burglar had taken, whether east, west, north, or south; only that he was off somewhere.

The affair was entrusted to me, but I wanted that indispensable condition of hope – the certainty, or at least probable suspicion, of his being in Edinburgh.

However, I transferred the image of the fellow to my mind's eye by that inside photography I have a knack in. I never knew where the light comes from, but the image, if once there, does not need any "gall" of anger to fix it, rather only the honey of love. I had him set up in that inside-plate accordingly, as large and living as life: six feet two, dark complexion, leg-of-mutton whiskers, drooping nose, as if too heavy for the forehead to sustain, small mouth under the same, sadly oppressed by the said nose, and as if afraid to open under so formidable an incumbrance, and something of a squint, under a bush of eyebrow. As for clothes, uncertain, unless he exchanged in the morning, and put on the new greatcoat and boots, which, for the sake of completing the picture, I supposed he had done; and so I had my man's image safe in my mind's keeping. But where was the original? I have always had a yearning for those comparisons, however odious, between the mind-sun-picture and the real walking, breathing piece of humanity itself, however low and degraded; but the desire is fruitless without the one of the two sides of the comparison.

Two days passed without issue, and it was now Saturday night. I had had the image all right for twice twenty-four hours, but where was the lantern? Even that would shew me the honest man in the dark, – more difficult then to be seen, though present, than at noonday, as in the old case; nor have we more of that class now than then, I suspect. I wanted my "idea," and it was not a case exactly of time; another day might as well pass without diminishing my chance of success. I would wait for my "idea," just as the poets do, I'm told – not considering themselves bound to work unless they're sure they have it, though some tell me that many try without it. Better they than I, for I never did any good without mine. It might come by chance. True, what have I not done, in my small way, by chance? Ay, but Chance never smiled on me unless I poked her (is she female?) some way; so that my "notion," after all, has been, in the getting of it, my own work, only perfected by a higher hand.

In this dubious, stupid kind of state I left the Office, intending to go home; nor, before I came to Toddrick's Wynd, had I any intention to poke up my favourite goddess; but, just as I was passing by the entry, my right leg I found inclined to the south, and the one leg carried the other, and both my head, which, so drowsy was I, seemed to be quite guiltless of the change from my right line home to bed down that same close. Habit, I fear, had some part in this wilfulness of my lower members. A Mrs Taylor lived down the wynd, a famous keeper of a half-respectable kind of lodging-house – a species of pool whence I have drawn many a kipper, as well as full-roed fish, newly run, with no other bait than a sombre "March-dun" or sober "May-bee" – and with a lazy floating line, too, without a bit of harling or whipping. Yes, I had been so often there, that I might be said to have formed a habit of going, for that kind of comfort without which I do not think I could live in this world of man-and-woman wickedness.

Having opened the good woman's door, – I call her good, because, if her lodgers were often only half-respectable, she was wholly so, at least in my eyes, – I entered with my usual familiarity, and sat down with her by the fire. I have said I wanted comfort, and so I began my old way of asking for it.

"Any lodgers just now?"

"Ay, a man frae the country. He came early in the morning, and got his breakfast. He is to sleep a' night at ony rate."

"What like is he?" I inquired.

"A perfect Anak amang the Philistines! Ye're a guid buirdly man yersel'; but, my faith! ye're naething to him. The man, I fancy, is guid eneugh; but I wadna redd you meddle him – I mean if he were ane ye had ony care for – without at least twa assistants."

"Can you describe his face?" said I, really in the expectation of getting nothing.

"Indeed, no," replied the good woman, "for it's lang since I gave up spying into men's faces, whaur I never, in my best days, saw muckle to look at, but a nose amang a bush o' hair, and twa een aye glowerin' at us women-folk; but, besides, my niece Jenny gave him his breakfast, and I've scarcely seen him; – but, Guid save us! here he is," she added, as she heard a heavy foot in the lobby.

And so, to be sure, the big lodger entered, very confidently, drew in a chair, and sat down. I threw my eye over him on the instant, not of course very inquiringly, – for, indeed, as I have already said, a glance generally does my purpose, – and there was the nose, so much too heavy-like for the forehead, and the mouth under the incumbrance of the nose, the leg-of-mutton whiskers, and the squint, all so perfect, that my mind-sun-image leapt within me, as if it would be out to its original, there to lose itself in flesh and blood. Enough for the justification of my modesty and simplicity, and taking-it-soft method – nay, I'm not sure if the man had observed whether I looked at him at all or not, and, as for the future of our companionship, I did not need. I had something else to do – I had caught my "idea," as well as its original; but then the one was a fancy, and the other a "Tartar".

The conversation was meanwhile leading to trades and occupations; how it began I cannot tell; but all of a sudden it came into my head to say to my man, "You'll be a hawker, no doubt?"

"Are *you* a hawker?" replied he, rather in a surly tone, as if offended.

"Yes," said I.

"I thought as much," growled he, "for we think everybody we meet should be like ourselves."

"And yet we don't find that always," I rejoined, softly. "But I could wish every man were as well to do as I am, for I have six men on the road, and a horse seldom off it."

"The horse will be for yourself?" said he.

"Yes; I could not get on without my Rory; for, you know, I have all those six fellows to look after."

"Why, don't they return at the end of their rounds?" inquired he, again.

"Yes, if they are able."

"And what's to disable them?"

"The fiend drink," said I, somewhat sorrowfully. "They get into wayside publics, and sometimes lie for days – all the while my goods are being stolen."

"And what do you do with them when you find them in this state?" said he. "Turn them off, I fancy, and get more sober men?"

"No: were I to do that, I would be changing every week, and with no chance of getting better ones; for if they don't drink, they cheat, and a drunken honest pedlar is better than a sober dishonest one."

"Why, then, you must just let them sleep off their drink," said he, "and trust to a sober run to make up for the drunken one?"

"No; I hasten to the spot, and having caught the fellow as he begins to look clear, I handcuff him, and bring him into town with the pack on his back. There I relieve him, and keep him without wages as a punishment, just as long as I think necessary; and when I think he is determined to do better, I give him his pack again, and begin his pay."

"And is this strange punishment often necessary?" said he, as his curiosity became excited by my novel method.

"Why," replied I, "no longer ago than Wednesday morning, I was obliged to set off for Peebles, where one of my chaps was lying drunk – and I think I met you" (a chance thrust) "coming out of the town with a bundle, and that was just the very reason that made me suppose you were one of our order."

"Well," said he, thus taken suddenly, "I did leave Peebles on Wednesday morning with a bundle, but I am not a hawker."

"No offence; it is a good honest calling. Once upon a time a great part of the country trade of Scotland was done by hawking, and a pedlar was often worth thousands."

"Maybe," said my giant; "but if I were one of your men I would be very drunk indeed if you could handcuff me."

"Perhaps I wouldn't try one of your size and mettle," said I, "unless you were very drunk."

"And then what the use?" rejoined he. "Drunkenness is a very good handcuffing itself, though I never saw the instrument I have heard so much of, nor would I like to deserve it. But, man," he continued, after a pause, during which he perhaps thought he did deserve the application of the check, and maybe shook a little at the prospect of feeling it, "what are handcuffs – what like are they? Could a strong man not snap them, and then snap his fingers at the officer?"

"A very simple thing," said I, drawing out a good specimen, which I cherish as my stock-in-trade, maybe with no less affection than Simpson did his bit of hemp, though, in point of respectability, I don't want the two things to be compared. "Here is my wrist-curb for my disobedient pedlars."

I even put the thing into his hands.

"A very simple affair," said he, with a sneer; "but I am d——d if that would hold me, unless it be applied in some queer way."

"Well," said I, "I never saw one of my men break it or get loose."

"How *do* you apply it?" said he, looking curiously.

"Why, just this way."

And in, I hope, my usual kindly manner, I put his right hand into the kench.

"How is that to bind a man?" he again sneered.

"Not finished yet, my dear fellow. I bind the other end to my *left* hand thus, and there you are."

"Well, rather kittle, I admit," said he, looking not quite comfortable-like; "and I would just as soon be out of it."

"But you have not tried it yet," continued I. "Sometimes a man is unfortunate, and while we are yet innocent and free we might be nothing the worse for preparing for an eventual future, you know. Just suppose that I were not a hawker, but one of those very uncomfortable men called detective officers, and that I wanted to walk you up to the Cross. Let us see – come along, now; quietly, my good fellow – this way" – leading him out – "so, this way – so," till I got him to the outer door leading to the close. "So, how quiet you are! You don't resist. Why don't you? So" – up the close a bit – "you said you could snap it, or get loose, and then snap your fingers, and yet don't, you see?"

Even all this time my man thought it play, but whether it was that suspicion seized him, or he merely wanted to try the game, I cannot say, but he began in earnest to struggle; but it would not do. I held him firm by the right arm, and whenever he used the left, I quelled him easily by *my* right.

"Enough of it," said he, at last.

"Not just yet," said I, with an *impressive* softness. "I want to see if I can take you up as far as the Police Office."

"The Police Office!" he roared, with a tremendous growl. "The Police Office and be d——d! Why there?"

"To be searched and examined," I replied, still keeping my temper, "and perhaps committed for breaking open your old master's house at Peebles, on Wednesday night, and stealing, among other things, the greatcoat that's now on you, and, I believe, also the boots now on your feet."

I felt his right arm fall as if palsied. I could see by the lamp at the head of the close that he was as pale as pipeclay. There was not so much pith in this big man as would have sufficed to break a rosin-end of good hemp, nor did he speak a single word. All I heard was his labouring breath, as he heaved his strong ribs, so that he might give room for the play of his heart. I was now safe from an attempt at escape, for we had reached the top of the wynd, where the man in charge of the street immediately came up to my assistance. But somehow I got filled with the demon of pride. I had an ambition to walk him up alone, and though, no doubt, the appearance of the policeman might have contributed to the continuance of my now easy victory, yet I verily believed he was still incapable – such is often the effect of that striking down of the confidence and courage of a conscious criminal, by a calm announcement, coupled with a mere strap of leather – of offering any resistance.

And thus I took him to the room of the lieutenant, where Captain Stewart happened to be at the time; and here it was he first found voice.

"I am brought here by a hawker. I am not one of his pedlars, and no more drunk than he is himself," he cried, his mind suggesting some faint hope which, for a moment, blinded him to his fate.

"Why, McLevy, you have caught our Peebles friend," said the captain, laughing, but wondering, too, at my new vocation of pedlar; "there's the height, the nose, and all the rest, as large as life. Where, in the name of all that's wonderful, did you find him?"

"Stranger still," said the lieutenant, "where's your assistant? You couldn't handcuff that giant alone?"

"He's handcuffed, anyhow," said I; "call some of the men, for I want to be relieved."

He was, in a few minutes, safer still – locked up for the night.

Don't, I beg of you, suppose that we are such ill-disposed and gloomy beings, who frequent this outer chamber or entrance to the dempster's hall, that we never have the luxury of a little quiet mirth. Bless you all, except, of course, those who will not come quietly up to see us, we are quite humane in our way – no hyena's laugh or crocodile's tears amongst our fraternity. We can even enjoy such mishaps as the discomfiture of those who try to put mirth to flight in many a domestic heaven; and can even afford, without detriment to our hearts, to be merry over grief, when it is the grief which follows God's behest against the disturbers of man's rest. Then it is only making the balance even, for how glorious do our enemies, whom we yet treat as friends, get in their midnight triumphs of pilfering, robbing, and murdering their fellow-creatures, who not only never injured them, but often served them well, but, alas! not wisely. So I need no apology for that heartily-passed half-hour, during which I explained the capture of my man – one of my six pedlars; but withal, it was nothing but the confidence my superiors had in me that prevented them doubting, not only the means I employed in getting the wrist of this truly big thief into the strap, but my ability to bring so great a giant all so quietly from Toddrick's Wynd to the Cross of Edinburgh. I was at least comforted, even by Widow Taylor, at whose house I had sought consolation for my two days' disappointment, and went home to bed without a touch of compunction.

Next day, my pedlar, with his pack – collected from several brokers – along with him, was sent to Peebles, where the Sheriff and Jury gave him nine months, to confirm him in a resolution, no doubt formed when he pled guilty, that he would not, even at the bidding of a hawker, try on a pair of handcuffs again.

The Conjuror

THE MORE I consider my eventful life, the more I am satisfied that there are coincidences that cannot be explained on the common calculations of Chance, because, though I have attributed many of my lucky hits to her, whom I call my patroness, yet I am quite sure her ladyship, though by no means a Lady Bountiful, is very much a Lady Grateful, who insists on something being done by her favourites to deserve her attention – perhaps a little flattery, though I am not much in that way.

About 1810, a very young boy, in Bo'ness, was sent by his masters, – shipowners, I think, there, – with £200 to place in the bank to their credit. As he went along, he was met by a man, holding a good character, and following the profession of a schoolmaster. Seized, it must have been, by the very demon of ambition, or perhaps sick of unbreeching and birching, – which seemed to do no good in the world, as the people were all as bad notwithstanding as he felt himself to be in his heart, in spite of all the birching he himself had got, – he fell upon the boy, who, he had suspected, was the bearer of money, and by sheer force took the whole sum from him. How, in so small a place, and at noon-day, he could have escaped, is a mystery I never heard cleared up, but true it is he did escape from the town, notwithstanding of the hullaballoo that got up in the neighbourhood. If he had taken to any of the country-leading roads, especially that to Edinburgh, he would have been seized; and I have always held the probability to be, that he sought refuge in some of the low, disreputable houses, where the inmates have a strong sympathy for custodiers of cash, so long as it lasts, thereafter kicking them out, and "serve 'em well."

We got, of course, information; but, after some weeks, I concluded that the man had either never come to Edinburgh, or had quickly left it. His crime was there, however, where it made a considerable noise from its peculiarity; for though dominies have often vices, it is seldom they betake themselves to the highway. When I know a man is not under the changeful wing of an alibi, he must be got of course, that's certain. That's a rule with me; but never having considered myself omniscient, the moment I am satisfied a man is not on my beat I can be easy. But then my beat was certainly a pretty wide one, and the difficulty was to find out one negative among so many positives as some two hundred thousand; and somehow I am a hard hoper, so that my conclusion was rather a forced matter in this case.

About a week or ten days after the affair, I was one night taking a turn along Bristo Street, a little in the knight-errant way, looking out for some pretty Lady Virtue, in defence of whom, under the brutalities of her ungallant sons, I might break, not a spear, but a head. On the pavement there stood two young girls, speaking, with their bonnets nid-nodding against each other, and looking with eyes so scandalously full of scandal of some very captivating kind, that I was induced to stop.

"What now, my lasses?"

"Fine night."

"Where do you belong to, now? Edinburgh lasses, eh?"

"No, Bo'ness," said one of them.

"Bo'ness! Oh, you must have heard of the school-master who robbed the boy?"

"Ay, and just speakin' o' him," said the second.

"Do you know him?" asked I, just with the proper carelessness.

"Brawly; he has whipt me before now, and I wadna care though he was hanged in his ain lang tawse, for his cruelty to me mony a day."

"Well, perhaps I may help you, to repay him," said I; "one good turn deserves another."

Thereupon one, shooting out her face so as to be very near my ear, said, "Whisht!"

"Why? There's no one near."

"Nae saying; he's in that public house there," pointing with her finger.

"Stop there till I come," said I, and instantly walked in.

I got into a room where there was a man, threw my eye over him, and there to be sure was Mr ——. I took no time to scan; you only raise suspicion. A glance gave me the "nose somewhat turned up," the "demure face," as if so tired of whipping urchins; "grey eye," far ben, so indicative of foxiness; "big upper lip," of sensuality; "no whiskers," where whiskers should *have been*; and, beyond all, the look of great reverence, as if he had been bred to psalm-singing.

"Fairish night," said I.

"Middling," was the gruff reply of my schoolmaster.

"Bring me a bottle of ginger beer," I cried, suddenly, to the man of the house.

If any one will guess why I called for a drink I despised on a coldish night, when perhaps I needed something to warm me under the freezing look of his reverence, I'll give him my baton. Just guess now, and fail. It was not, I assure you upon my honour, that I might treat the girl whom he had whipped. Be so good as keep that in mind, because you might call me a fool for proposing a puzzle which was no puzzle.

My beer came in, and, going to the door, I brought in the whipped Jenny.

"Take a little beer, lass," said I, cheerfully. But she couldn't, for her eyes were fixed on the dominie, – in the recollection probably of the tawse, – and her whole body shook.

"No fear," said I; "no tawse here, lass."

But still she stared and he stared, and they would have kept staring until all the froth on the beer had passed into thin air, if I had not put an end to it.

"You know the man?" said I to the girl.

"Ay – that's him," replied she, still staring at him, as if the old charm of the tawse tingled somewhere about her body.

"Who?" rejoined I.

"Mr ——, the schoolmaster o' Bo'ness."

"Well, give me your name and address," said I, getting out my pencil, and proceeding to make the important entry in that terrible red book of mine. "Now, my bonny lass," continued I, "your name is *given up* to the dominie, who'll *decry* you; but never mind. You may go now, but still remember me.'"

And she went, still all of a tremble, and forgetting her beer entirely.

"Well, I have the pleasure of having before me Mr ——, late schoolmaster at Bo'ness!"

"It's false, sir."

"At any rate a supposition's no crime, and just let us suppose it."

"I'm not to suppose any such thing."

"Don't want you – it isn't necessary. It is only necessary that I should, and, what is more, *I do*. And I also suppose you have something in your pocket which would be very interesting to me."

"I am a respectable man –"

"I'm not disputing it."

"And I see no authority you have to inquire what I carry with me."

"Well, you may put me down as impertinent. I am sorry for it, but I am often obliged to be uncivil – can't really help it. Turn out."

"'Twill do you no good," said he, sulkily, and fumbling in his breeches pocket.

"There's all the money I have," – putting some silver upon the table, – "if you're a robber, take it."

"I don't happen to belong to that fraternity, I am a robber-catcher."

I had got the *whip*-hand of the reverend dominie. He shook violently, and knit his brows to make amends.

"You are pale, my good sir," said I, "and my beer's done, but I see you have got some in your coat pocket," – pointing to the top of a bottle sticking out, and which I had seen when I called for my own, through sympathy or fun; for we sometimes, when prosperous in our calling, get merry at the expense of vice. And why not? Art we not men? Have we not eyes, noses, hearts to feel, and lungs to laugh, and all the rest?

"What mean you?" he said, looking at me as if those far-ben eyes had come an inch out of their dark holes.

"Just to give you a drop of your favourite beverage," said I, pulling out a bottle from his right pocket, "Ah! And here is one for me as well," taking another from the left; "and here's a third for Madam Justice," taking the remaining one from his breast pocket.

"I get beer at this house," said he, "and bring back the bottles to get more."

Here I was certainly a little taken aback. The explanation was really plausible, and I thought for a moment my drollery had been folly – that however brisk the beer I had called for, my joke had been stale.

"And now you see," said he, profiting by my disadvantage, "what you have made of your impudence."

But then, I think I have said that Vice is liable to infirmities. When she gets merry she gambols, like the moth, and rushes into the candle; or crows like the cock, who, getting on the heap-top, and then into the claws of the eagle, would never, but for the cocky-leerie-la of his jubilation, have been seen by his big friend. Yes, my reverence here committed a mistake; – probably though he had not, I would have been up with him. And then, with all the coolness in the world, he actually took up one of the bottles, and was putting it into his pocket.

"What! Didn't you say you had brought these empty bottles! – for that they are empty," I continued, as I lifted one, "there can be no doubt; and why put them back into your pocket again to trouble you by taking them out a second time?"

"That's my business," said he.

"And this is mine," said I, taking up a poker in one hand and a bottle in the other, and knocking the head and upper part clean off, when there appeared a nicely rolled up bundle of notes, about £50.

The sound of the broken bottle brought in the landlord.

"Just in time," said I, taking the man by the coat, and drawing him forward.

"You see this? – it may be necessary you testify to it. This bottle, which I have taken from this gentleman, is more wonderful than that one I have read of in *The Devil on Two Sticks*, for it contains this bundle of notes. Let us try our luck again," I continued, as I broke the second, and then the third, each revealing a similar bundle of notes, amounting in all to upwards of £150.

"Do you put pound-notes in your ginger beer bottles when you cork them up for sale?"

The man laughed, even in the midst of his bewilderment. "The devil o' the like o' this ever I saw!" he said; "what is the meaning of it? Ah, I see, you're a conjuror."

"Just so."

"I wish you would conjure some of my bottles that way. Faith, an' I'd soon be a rich man."

"I only do it to my friends," I replied, as I took a look of Master Reverence; "but no more of this joking; you have seen what you have seen, and can speak to my conjuring when you are called upon by an officer from the Sheriff."

The man began to see a little better.

"I understand," said he. "Well, you may go."

"And now, sir," addressing my prisoner, "you will please go with me to the Police Office; I will take care of your bottles."

"What to do there?" he said, scarcely now able to speak with fear.

"To answer to the charge of robbing the boy – in Borrowstounness, a week ago."

I now began to gather up my broken bottles; and as I proceeded, I heard him sighing and breathing laboriously; words came too, as if he had forgotten I was there. The spirit was working within; the conscience up in war, tearing him; he threw himself back on the chair, with his legs out, and as he hauled these shuffling along the floor, he still muttered – I could scarcely make it out, yet I was satisfied of these strange words, which I have never forgotten, and never will forget …

"Good God! This very girl I punished severely without a fault, because I had a grudge against her father!"

So, so, I thought; and what hand led me here so that I should come upon this girl, and what power stopped me, what power opened my mouth? Silence! I am only a humble instrument for discovering the secret ways of man's wickedness. Yes, I have often been impressed with this feeling when people thought I was merely pleased with my own poor efforts. Maybe they did not know me, for these thoughts are not just suited for the Police Office; and then, I have been obliged to stand the look of great judges, who, while they complimented me, no doubt looked upon me as a poor machine, only moved by strings pulled by a love of being thought clever, while they, who act upon my detections, are so wise and so honourable. But every man to his trade – shoemaker, poet, judge, and last – excuse me – the ferreter out of evil. It is easy to "charge" on such labours as mine, – easy to pronounce the word guilty, as proved by them, – easy to hang, as a consequence of them; and yet no man has less reason to complain than I myself.

"I love a penitent," said I, as I turned round to the miserable man.

He did not relish the compliment; such people never do.

"Mind your own business; you have been insolent in your wit."

Ah, there's no pleasing them: if you are harsh, they say you are riding over them; if mild, you are gloating over your superiority; if humorous, you are cruel and ironical.

"Suppose then," said I, "I command you as a suspected —"

"Just suspected."

"As a suspected robber of a poor helpless boy, not much beyond your birch —"

"Peace, man; your words enter my soul."

"Who might have been suspected of having appropriated that money, and been ruined for ever, to —"

"Peace, peace!"

"Walk up to justice; – will that please you?"

"True, true!" he ejaculated; "what will please him who has displeased God, and therefore himself? Were you to speak as an angel, I would call you devil; and devil you are!"

"Well, you will admit that the boy's masters, when they get the contents of the bottles, will not have so bad an opinion of me; you know there's a reward."

"But none to me," he sobbed, as his head fell on his breast; "my reward will not be here."

"Not sure but it may begin here, and in a way which may lead you to rejoice that it does not end here. A little sharpness quickens a man's conscience, and when that begins to cry out, you know there's a voice that answers."

"Well, you are not so bad a fellow after all," he said; and, rising, "now I will go with you quietly, for I think God's mind is in me, and perhaps He may lead me through tribulation to exultation."

"But what put the bottles in your head!" said I, changing the subject, for really I felt curious, though I have seen all manner of hiding places, even the tender armpits of women, – yes, their mouths speaking sweet, endearing words, – but a ginger beer bottle was new to me.

"Because," replied he, "after my first run I got thirsty, and having, in a public house, got a drink of ginger beer, and as the empty bottle stood before me, I thought it would be a good means of hiding. No doubt the devil put this in my head, because he knew there was a man in Edinburgh who understood the devil's ways, and would find me out. But what," he asked, after a pause, "made you call for ginger beer when you entered? The words went to my very heart."

"Because," said I, "the devil induced you to allow a neck to stick out. I suspected in an instant that the money was there."

"Strange, indeed!"

"And I was so amused with myself, that I called for a bottle, just as a playful way – for I do my business with good humour – of intimating to you that I knew your trick."

We had talked more than I am in the habit of doing generally. I took him, with the broken bottles and notes, up to the Office.

"There," said I, to the Captain, "is the Bo'ness gentleman, and there is the money – all but fifty pounds – and there are the bottles where the money was secreted."

These were enigmas, but when the Captain understood them, he did not know what to say, between a desire to laugh and some restraint he could not comprehend.

"Ah!" said he, at last, "McLevy, we should have a pulpit here, where people might be taught by us, as preachers, that God has many ways of finding out the wicked."

The prisoner was sent on to Linlithgow, along with the notes and broken bottles, and afterwards sentenced to fourteen years. The Judge complimented me handsomely; not so the offerers of the reward, for they never gave me a penny. The £25 went to the girls. I did not begrudge the gift; and yet, somehow, though not fond of money, more than is necessary for my humble wants, I think I should have got a five-pound note to wet my throat with ginger beer when following up the devil.

The Swan

THE GENIALITIES of the most genial of us are not eternal; and I have found this in my own case, – not because my kindliness has been so often scorned, or received with anger if not oaths, but on another account, which the reader will scarcely suspect. We have all heard of the madman who went to the doctor at Morningside, and, with a grave face, opened his subject with –

"Sir, I am concerned about Mr ———," (the keeper).

"Why?" answered the doctor.

"He is in a very bad way, sir."

"In what respect?"

"That's for you to find out, sir. It is for me, who hope I am a humane man, to take prompt measures for his benefit, or I'll not answer for the consequences. I do enough to give you the hint. It is necessary, in the first place, that you shave his head; secondly, that you submit him to the shower-bath; thirdly, that you should bleed him freely; fourthly, that you should purge him; fifthly, that you bind him down with strong ropes to his bed; and, sixthly, that you set watchers over him, of whom, for humanity's sake, I am willing to be one.

I discharge my duty in making this announcement; and if my advice is not followed, you will abide by the consequences."

The keeper, though a genial man, could not have suffered all this without being angry. Neither could I resist a feeling of indignation at an act of a similar kind on the part of those under my charge.

For some time, in 1836, I was aware that many pockets were picked by two of the most cunning of their tribe I ever met, George or Charles Holmes (I forget which) and Angus McKay. They went always together; and if they had by their cunning resisted or baulked me, – nay, if they had even stood up to fight me, – I might still have retained my temper; but all the while the people were sending us charges, with complaints of emptied pockets, they were busy taking care of me. I believe, if they had had their will, I would have been shaved, bathed, bled, purged, bound, and watched; but their care was limited to the last. When I went home at night, I observed that they regularly followed me, saw me housed, and then went to play in their old way of lightening the pockets of the lieges. Nor were they content with seeing me home – they actually posted a companion of the name of Bryce, who went by the name of "The Watcher", to hang about my stair-foot all the evening; so that when "The Watcher" was not visible by them while plying their art on the Bridges, they could make certain that I was not in the way.

This was to my temper rather too much. I never cared for patronage, but these honours were hard to bear; and what made it worse was, that they thought I was utterly ignorant of all this care taken of me, just as if they were satisfied with the consciousness that "virtue is its own reward". I bear only to a certain extent, like the most patient, and that extent was reached. On a certain day, when I knew their pockets were absolutely filled with the results of their successes of the previous night, I observed them at their old patronising care. There they were after me, with "The Watcher" on the other side; nor did they leave me till they saw me safe in my house, at the foot of the Old Fishmarket Close, in the Canongate. For this kindness I could repay them in another way than by being excessively angry at them. They would be busy that night in adding industriously to their store, and my opportunity was apparent.

After taking my tea, I sat down and wrote a note to my assistant –

"Send down an officer, and take up Bryce, whom you will find hanging about my stair-foot, and give him in charge at the Office; then dress in plain clothes, and, with another man also plain, wait for me below the south arch of the bridge, at seven."

This note I despatched in a basket, carried by a girl who lived ben in the adjacent flat, and proceeded to effect as good a transformation in myself as would enable me to pass for a countryman come in to Hallow Fair (then being held,) with, it was to be hoped, a hundred pounds or two upon him, received for stirks, in a pocket-book in the outer breast-pocket of his rough coat.

I was at my post by seven, and found my faithful assistant very well changed, and his companion along with him. I opened my plans to them, after being satisfied that "The Watcher" was safe. We then mounted the long stair leading to the North Bridge. We then separated, but only on the condition that we should never lose sight of each other. The streets were much crowded, in consequence of the fair. The big gudgeons, all supplied with the money derived from their sales, were stalking about; the mermaids were trying their fatal charms in every direction – not combing their own hair at so busy a time, but rather trying to tie that of their victims; and the sharks were plentiful, greedy, and shy as ever. There was that night more of concert between the two latter than we find in books of natural history, where they are represented as working on their own individual hook; but otherwise they were true to their kind: the yellow-haired sirens, when they got a victim in their arms, plunging with him to their caves – not pure coral – and there devouring him in the dark; and the blue sharks gobbling them up just where they caught them, – the one courting embraces, and the other shying them, but both equally fatal.

Of the real blue kind there were my patrons and keepers, Holmes and McKay – sharp, active, and hopeful – turning up their bellies every now and then, as they tried a bite. They were sure "The Watcher" was not to be seen, and therefore I could not be seen either; neither was I; and hence their confidence, and hence, too, mine. Perhaps the pleasure of that condition called *incognito* – into which, I rather suspect, all men and women, when their eyes have been glared upon by the disturbing sun of curiosity or notoriety, love to glide – was equal on both sides. Ay, where is the man and woman without their occasional mask? If you search well, you will *detect*, not only the skeleton which is behind the green curtain over the recess in every house, but also the mask which is in some spring-guarded drawer in the bureau, – often beneath the pillow, – sometimes at the back of the death-bed, when the parson (who has one often in his pocket) is praying over the expiring wretch; sometimes it is put into the coffin along with the corpse, so that no one shall ever know what deeds he or she, who looks so calm and innocent there, was doing for the sixty years of their pilgrimage in this world of masks.

Opposite Mr Craig's shop, my attention was for a little taken off my two friends – it was not yet my time to renew my acquaintance with them – by the attraction of "The Swan", a long-necked nymph, who was doing "Charlie [Holmes] is my darling", in a very good street style, to an admiring circle extending over the pavement. She was a true *Vesuvienne*, and a good devourer of the gold-fish, probably from that fine, long, white neck of hers; nor had I seen her at the minstrel trade before. Why now, when, in place of halfpennies and pennies – which I knew she despised – she might have been, like her companions of the lava streets, picking up crown-pieces, or perhaps pounds, which had been given for fat gimmers or stots in the forenoon? The question was only to be answered by me, and it was not a difficult one. I saw Holmes and McKay among her crowd, paying great attention to her siren strains – "The Swan" was not dying just then – that is, with their eyes; and, then, hands and fingers are not necessary to the enjoyment of good music. Nay, it was even with a little humour in his small grey eye that Holmes went and put something into her hand, very likely a small portion of the price of the foresaid gimmers and three-year-olds; and you could not have detected in "The Swan's" looks the slightest difference between the gratitude conferred on the giver and that with which she favoured some stalworth Peeblesshire feeder, who wanted to shew his admiration of Charlie and "the darling" at the same time, by giving her a penny.

I have said it was only I that could explain this. "The Swan" was the "fancy" of Holmes, and her singing on the street was just the *treble* of his *base* on the pavement. She collected the crowd, and he collected the money from the crowd, without the trouble of "Please, sir, help the poor girl," – "A penny, sir, for the singer," – or simply, "Please, sir." All that was unnecessary, when the fingers were even more subtle than the tongue. To say the truth, I was amused by the play, even to the suspending for a time my own proper part of the performance, if I did not entirely forget my anger at my patrons. Certainly, though I saw some smaller actors in the walking-gentleman line trying to do a bit of business, I had no heart for watching their pickeries, so insignificant by the contrast of the true Jeremys. I did not even notice our worthy captain, who, as he was passing to the Office, stood for a moment listening to the assiduous damsel, as innocent of all this by-play that was going on, with his favourite McLevy in the *rôle*, as if he had been one of the bumpkins from the grazing hills himself. It was not just then convenient to renew my acquaintanceship with him, so I let him enjoy himself a little, with the intention probably of reminding him next day of the figure he was cutting as a dummy, though the sharpest head in the city. At length he left, to resume his arduous duties in the High Street; and it was for me to let him go, if I was not glad of his departure, from a place where his presence could only interrupt, not only the playful tricks of my patrons, but my own.

But I must now act; to delay longer was to run a risk of being foiled, for so many good opportunities for the transference of pocket-books presented themselves, that my friends might succeed in a great effort, and be off, contented with their booty, without bestowing any attention on me. My assistant was behind me, and still kept his eye on me. I became still more entranced by the strains of "The Swan"; nor was Holmes – whom I now contrived to get near – less captivated. Though not requiring much elevation of the head, I was so intent upon catching every note of her voice, that I stood on tiptoe, looking over the heads of those before me, and with no more attention to that valuable pocket-book of mine – so proud of its contents that it poked its head out of its place – than merely sufficed to let me know that it was taken away. Could Holmes resist so ardent a gudgeon, entranced by a living, not a dying swan? Not likely, when he was, by my skill, just alongside of me, with McKay behind him, to get handed to him, if he could, that same pocket-book which was determined also to be in the play. I never put on a pair of handcuffs in a kindly way with more pleasure in the touch than I now permitted Holmes' hand to have its own way. My book was off in a moment, but not given to McKay before my assistant had Holmes in his grasp. The other policeman seized McKay.

The strains of "The Swan" were hushed; nor did she begin again; she was too much affected to be able to sing when her tender mate was in the claws of the eagles. I was the victim, and required to keep up my character, in which I gained a kind of honour, or rather sympathy, which I had never before had an opportunity of enjoying. The crowd, many of whom were Hallow-Fair men, crowded about me, inquiring how much money was in my pocket-book; and I was in the humour.

"A hundred pounds; the price of six three-year-olds, and all I'm worth in the world."

"Might have been me," said another, "for I've as muckle in my book."

"But, Lord, how cleverly the villains have been nabbed," said a second.

"They'll no try that game again," rejoined a third.

All which I heard very pleasantly as I proceeded, still the victim along with the captors. Meanwhile my assistant retained the pocket-book, which he had caught as Holmes was on the eve of throwing it away. As yet neither of the fellows had recognised either me or my assistant, and they were indignant at being seized by unofficial personages; nor did they know in whose hands they were till they were fairly before the captain, who, as we entered, was sitting altogether oblivious of "The Swan's" strains, whatever effect they might have produced upon him while listening to them.

"Sir," said I, as I stood before him, keeping my face as much from my patrons as I could; "I have been robbed of my pocket-book, wi' the price o' a' my three-year-olds, by thae twa vagabonds there."

"Why, these are old offenders, I suspect," said the captain, not very well able to restrain himself, as he looked in my face and recollected how I had been watched and annoyed by them; "but I hope your money's safe. Let me see the pocket-book;" and getting it from Mulholland and opening it, "The price of all your stock, good sir; why, there's nothing in it but rags and paper!"

"Sold for nothing, by God!" said Holmes to McKay.

"More than your value," said I, turning round, and looking them straight in the face, in the midst of the laughter of the men; "and yet not so cheap as you think; search them."

A process not so soon accomplished, for out of every pocket there came various waifs, some of them singular enough; a net purse with two sovereigns and a penny, a small clasp leather one with some shillings, three or four handkerchiefs, two or three pound-notes crumpled up, a number of shillings and coppers, a lady's wig-frontlet carefully rolled up in a piece of paper, and other curiosities.

"We will get customers for all these tomorrow," said I; "so that it will not be necessary for the farmer to charge you for the price of the beeves."

"Who could have thought that it was the rascal himself?" muttered Holmes between his gnashing teeth.

"Ay, and he so snugly watched in the Old Fishmarket Close," said I, for a man has sometimes a pleasure to let an old friend know a grievance he (that friend) has put upon him. In short, I was for once revengeful in my humour, and what is the use of revenge unless the wrong-doer knows your triumph? "But we are not quite done yet," I continued; then, turning to my assistant, "Go to 'The Swan's' nest, and see if you can find any more of that kind of articles, – she may be a magpie in disguise."

"I only gave her a penny," said Holmes, sneeringly; "perhaps you'll find that. I've nothing to do with her."

"Beyond getting her to sing for a crowd you might work upon," added I. "You see you are scarcely masters for me; whom you took so much care of; but now I'll take care of you – lock them up."

And they were taken off, swearing and threatening in their rage and disappointment.

It was not long till my assistant brought in "The Swan", and with her a great number of valuable articles, of which she had been the resetter from Holmes. Many of them, on being compared with the books, answered the description of valuables robbed or stolen a good while before, and the charming singer was deposited in a suitable cage, where (*Charles* Holmes being her lover) she could sing, as she had done that night before, –

> *"Charlie is my darling,*
> *My young chevalier,"*

without adding *d'industrie*, for fear of hurting his feelings in the neighbouring cage. But by and by the tune was changed, when the Sheriff gave them their *terms* as old offenders, – not too hard terms either when it is considered how much anguish they had caused in many houses, not forgetting some anxiety in my own.

The Hay-Seeds

I HAVE HEARD it said that the clue of a man's destiny lies at the foot of his cradle. I don't pretend to understand this saying very well, but I know there is a clue that leads somewhere; and that although there may appear to be a break in it now and then, I have noticed the junction, where there seemed, to common eyes, to be no connexion whatever. I have already given a good many cases where the peculiar traces that bind a lawbreaker to his crime were so minute, that it seemed impossible to discover them; and if they had not been discovered, the destiny of the man could not have been said to be connected with the act, so that God's ways could not have been justified to man. But they were discovered, and hence our faith was confirmed. Of this kind of case, no one ever struck me as being more curious than that I am about to narrate, though the thing stolen was not, any more than in some other cases, of very great pecuniary value.

Some years ago, two or three young thieves were seen lurking about a house in Brandon Street, on a Saturday night. Their attention was directed to a front door, which no doubt they wished to be open. One was seen to go up and examine the checklock, and then come away and commune with his friends. Then there was a jingling of keys, as if they had been turning out their stock of skeletons to know which would fit. At length they succeeded: the old customer tried his hand again, the door was opened, and by and by the two who were on the watch outside got handed to them three topcoats, with which they made off, while the chief thief quietly shut the door and walked off. All this play was noticed by one who could neither run after them nor identify them; and when notice came to the Office, we had absolutely nothing to go upon.

Next morning (Sunday) Mr Wilson called the officers and gave them their commission. "It is not the value of the coats," he said, "that makes me anxious about this case, but the certainty I feel that if we don't get hold of the thieves, our books will be filled with cases of the same kind. Now let us see who shall be the first to bring in the gentlemen and the coats. I need not say," looking to me, "who I expect to be the man." I had confidence enough, and although there was no clue, I believe I smiled at the compliment, just as if I had said, "Well, Lieutenant, they shall be with you in a very short time." The truth is, that the theft was no sooner intimated, than my mind went away about Stockbridge, where I knew a covey of these wild-birds had alighted, and were picking up their food in the streets nearby; and my mind took this direction as a consequence of my experience that thefts by combination are generally traceable to a partnership which is as active while it lasts as it is short-lived. Nor are there many of these partnerships existing at a time, – sometimes only one, doing an amount of business, generally in the same line, which induces the good people to think the town is filled with robbers.

I and my coadjutors went together, going, by my leading, along Fettes Row, and intending to make some forenoon calls at Stockbridge. We had emerged by the side of St Stephen's Church, and just as we were on the eve of turning down by the front of it, I happened to cast my eye up Pitt Street, when my attention was arrested by two young men standing speaking to each other at the entry to the house and shop of a tailor in that street. One of the lads had his coat off, and I believe it was the white shirt-sleeves that first caught my eye.

"A little in the wildgoose-chase way," thought I, as I neared them, – "going to catch feathers from a plucked bird."

Notwithstanding, I proceeded, and just as I got within their eye-shot, – my own was discharged farther down, – one of the two made off up Pitt Street, but not before I discovered he was no other than one of my suspected at Stockbridge. The coatless one slunk in, and, leaving him safe enough, I made off after the fugitive. I traced him to the turn of Heriot Row, and saw him running west at full speed. It was Sabbath morning, and it was not for a decent person like me to be pursuing thieves on the Lord's day, though I was sure they were not running to church. So I turned my steps back to the tailor's shop, where my white-sleeved gentleman was now likely completing his toilet, to appear as gay as possible in presence of his Sunday-out housemaid, who would be ready for him as usual, about the time when her mistress would be thinking her devout Jenny would be walking churchward, to the sound of the Sabbath bells.

On getting downstairs, I knocked at a door, and straightaway there appeared before me my coatless customer, still uncoated and holding in his hand a big knife. The apparition startled me a little, but did not drive away my wits. I must get the knife out of his hand. He looked fierce, but that was no reason why I should not look the very opposite.

"Put on your coat," said I, "and come out and speak to me," – a process he could not very well have gone through with the gully in his hand.

Obedience to a soft request is natural, and my man, laying down the knife, with which, after all, he had perhaps been cutting his breakfast loaf, donned his coat, and came out to me, leaving the knife behind.

"Who was the lad you were speaking to a little ago at the door?" inquired I.

"I was speaking to nobody," replied he, with a very determined air, – a denial which resolved me at once. How much more I have often drawn out of a denial where the denied fact was clear, than I ever did out of an affirmation, though clenched with an oath!

"Now," said I, in pursuance of a resolution which

may appear unauthorised, if not foolhardy, but which I took my risk of, – for with me it has always been *no risk, no reward*, – "you take your hat, while I keep hold of you," remembering the knife, "and then I will take you where you may get some help to your memory."

And having kept hold of him till he was covered, I took him up the outside stair and committed him to one of my brethren, who quietly led him up to the Office.

Having despatched this worthy, I kept watch at the door until the officer returned, then betook myself to examine the nest from which I had taken my bird. At the foot of the stair I met an old man, the master of the youth, and, as I afterwards learned, his uncle. Though he had not formerly appeared, he had heard enough to satisfy him of what had been doing, and was clearly prepared for me.

"Though you have not often customers on Sunday morning," said I, "I have a commission for three topcoats, and want them upon the instant."

"I sell nothing on the Lord's day," replied my devout gentleman; "neither do I work on that day."

"But you are not forbidden to answer a plain question on that day," I rejoined; "and I ask you if you have about you three topcoats; and as you don't traffic today, I shall take them from you for nothing, to relieve your conscience."

"I have nothing of the kind," sulkily; "do you take me for a thief?"

"Not just yet," said I; "but wait there a little, and

perhaps I may do you that favour when I come upstairs."

And without waiting for an answer, I shot down a very tempting inner stair, leading to an underground kitchen at the bottom, and below the back of which, where there was a recess, I found the very things I was in search of. In all which proceedings, though there was a dash of haphazard, there were not wanting probabilities, which were at least sufficient to move me, and in the following of which I was thus rewarded.

"I will take you for a thief now," said I, as I came up the stair with the three coats over my arm. "Though you could not sell clothes on the Lord's day to a man, you could sell yourself to the devil by telling me a lie. These are the coats."

"Oh, they will be my nephew's, John Anderson," he cried.

"No matter, they have been found in your house, and you go with me."

And the devout little old man was so far cured of his devotion, that he neither preached nor prayed, probably because he had not a willing audience, and hypocrisy loses its cant before justice. He went quietly to where his nephew was; and now it was necessary to catch the other birds, who I suspected were those who brought the prey home. There was no difficulty about them; William Ferguson I had seen in the morning talking to Anderson; we got him on the same night at the house of his father. But there was another spoken to by John Anderson, as having been actively engaged in the robbery, – the brother of William Ferguson, called John. I had always such a desire to see my friends together, that it vexed me when any one was absent from a meeting, where the sympathy was generally so complete, that no one contradicted another, but all were bound together in the bonds of friendship, rendered tighter by a cause of common interest. If I had got none of the others, I would probably have been less solicitous about John; but John I must get, or my peace was not of that kind which consists in duty done. There was a difficulty about this John. I had never seen him, neither had any of my detective brethren; and that he had made a desperate bolt, there could be no doubt, having in all likelihood heard of the capture of Anderson in the fore-part of the day. Another officer considered he had got a string in the direction of Leith, because he had heard at the house of the father that they had friends in that quarter. I did not try to turn his nose, seeing he was holding it out so snuffingly in that direction, and accordingly allowed him to run on, with the only fear that the organ would stick in the earth, before he got to the burrow, so keen was he in testing the ground traces; so away he went.

As for myself, I had another notion. I have often found that Edinburgh thieves, when disturbed in their sweet security, make, like the deer, for the water, – not to swim, and distribute their peculiar odour in the fluid, but as a means to get away. And Fife is often the destination. Somehow they think policemen don't cross waters, – loving rather to search on dry land, after the manners of the bloodhounds, which are always at fault in lochs and streams. At any rate on this occasion, it came into my head that my friend John would make for Newhaven early in the following morning, to catch the steamer that then plied from that pier to Burntisland. So on Monday I got up before daybreak, or rather in the perfect darkness of the prior night not yet modified, and having dressed myself, I took my dreary way to the old fishing village. The day was beginning to break when I arrived at the pier, where I took my seat on the edge of one of the hauled-up boats. The fishermen had been down to the Isle of May, and having arrived with five or six cargoes of fish during the night, were all ready, in their thick pea-jackets, long boots, and red nightcaps, for the fish fair which is held on the pier almost every morning during the fishing season. The regular fishwomen were beginning to come down from the village, with their peculiar dress, – the loads of petticoats, of their favourite colours, yellow or red striped, with the indispensable pea-coat, and close mutch enclosed in a napkin. Then there came the crowds of the Edinburgh fish-hawkers, almost all young Irish hizzies, resonant of oaths, and each with the hurly, without which she could do nothing in her wandering trade.

By and by, the crowd, and noise, and hubbub increased to those of a regular fair; nor, amidst all the picturesqueness of the scene, was the indispensable fun wanting, – of such a piebald kind, too, with no similitude in the traits of the Irish jokes and the regular fishwives' Scotch humour, – yet with gradations of caste pervading the masses, the stately Newhaven dames appearing like grandees among the tattered callets of the High Street, and the demure and mute fishermen over-topping all, and only condescending to smile at times as some witty exclamation burst upon their ears. And there was I, sitting in the midst of this at six o'clock in the morning, looking for a young man I had never seen, and had only got described to me by an accomplice, who might have given me a lying portrait. What hope could I have of his being there, or of recognising him if he came? Not much; and yet enough, for the crowd being almost all women, I could devote my attention easily to a newcomer. The boat to Fife could be seen coming over the Firth on her way to Granton Pier, whence she would come to Newhaven, thence to start on her passage across. I was meanwhile busy enjoying the scene before me, not a little amused by the remarks of some of my High Street children, who knew me well enough, if more than one had not been through my hands. It was now their turn for revenge, –

"Och, woman, the thieves are so scarce in Edinburgh, he'll be to catch baddies this morning!"

"Ay, he'll to be handcuff the John Dories with a string."

"And maybe tak' them up to Haddie's (Haddo's) Hole, woman."

All which, and much more, I bore with good temper, the more by token I saw a young man coming sauntering down through the crowd, whose appearance claimed my special attention. He was very like the description given me by Anderson; yet my marks were so dubious, I could draw no very satisfactory conclusion. He paid no attention to the scene about him, and was clearly bent for the other side of the Firth, but he had no bundle, and had all the appearance of being on the "tramp" – not, however, as a tradesman on the search for work, but rather carrying to me the well-known aspect of one of our Edinburgh scamps, seedy, haggard enough, and clearly out-o'-sorts. He passed me as he went down, but the light of the morning was yet so hazy, that I required a nearer view. I rose from my seat, and followed him down the pier, getting as close to him as I could, with a view to a better comparison of his face with the image I had formed of him from Anderson's account. While thus examining him, I observed on his coat some hay-seeds. "That lad," thought I, "has had hay for his sheets;" and I then recollected that, in the grey dawn, I had observed a large hay-stack on the right side of the road coming down from Edinburgh. Slight as the suggestion was I felt myself certain that he had been sleeping in that hay-stack all night; and no one will betake himself to a bed of that kind without some motive of concealment or refuge. At least if he was not my John, he ought to have been; and every look, after the view of the seeds, seemed to send a back energy down through my arm, imparting something like a crave in the fingers to lay hold of him; but then I was among a crew of fish-women, who would have proved troublesome to me, from recollections of kindness received from me, either by themselves or some of their friends; and I required to have recourse to tact. So, going up to him carelessly, –

"Raw morning, my man."

"Ay," with some confidence, almost enough to shake the hay-seeds out of my mind.

"You'll be for Fife, I fancy?"

"Right," replied he; "when will the boat be here?"

"You'll see her near Granton, yonder; she'll be here in a quarter of an hour. We have time for a dram to keep the sea-air out of our empty stomachs."

And what eye that has been closed on a bed of hay in a raw night would not leap at the cheerful word "dram?" And so did his. Cold and breakfastless, he jumped at the offer.

"Come up to Wilson's," said I, "and I'll stand your glass besides my own."

And thus I managed him, for he had no notion but that I was an intended fellow-passenger. In two minutes after I had him seated in Wilson's, with the gill of whisky before us.

"Come, my lad," said I, – for truly I had some pity for him, so cold and heartless he looked, – "you will be the better for this."

And giving him his dram, and taking my own, of which I stood in some need as well, –

"Are you from Edinburgh?"

But here he faltered for the first time, even with the reviving whisky scarcely down his throat.

No; Cramond," said he, irresolutely.

And yet, if I was not mistaken, he came down the pier by the Fishermen's Square. I was now getting confidence, and he was not losing it. So I beat up my advantage, for I had no authority yet to take out my leather strap.

"It is strange how friends meet," said I, cheerfully. "I did not think that Jack Ferguson would have forgot an old fellow workman."

"Well, I don't remember you," said he, without a protest against my soft impeachment.

It is said that omission is not commission; a proverb not altogether true, I suspect, for here was just as good an admission that his name was John Ferguson as I could have wished in the very ardour of a search.

"And how is Bill, your brother?" said I, without telling him that I had lodged the said Bill in safe quarters on the previous night.

"Oh, well enough," he replied; and yet just with a trace of repentance that he had said it.

"Yes," said I, now perfectly sure of my man; "he is well enough, for he's in prison waiting for you, as his accomplice in a robbery of three coats, in Brandon Street, on Saturday night."

The words were not out when he started up, as if a cannon had been fired close by his ear, and made for the door.

"Come," said I, laying hold of him; "you can make nothing by flight in this thoroughfare; you may as well be easy. Here's a drop of whisky in the stoup yet. Take it kindly, and then I will fit you with these," taking out my cuffs.

And such is the accommodating spirit of these fellows, – so intimate with reverses, and mixing sin and sorrow with indulgence and indifference, – that Jack sat quietly down, and taking up the stoup, poured out the remaining half-glass, took it off, and then took on his curb.

"Well now, Jack," said I, for I was curious on a point, "didn't you sleep all night in the haystack up yonder, on this side of Bellfield?"

"Yes, I did," he replied; "how do you know that?"

"Why, by these hay-seeds on your jacket," said I. "Don't you see that if you had had these upon you last night before going to bed, and had taken off and put on your coat, as honest men do, these seeds would have been shaken off? And then, don't you further see, it was very unlikely you could have got these seeds upon you this morning, when newly out of bed? So, Jack," I continued, "it was really by seeing these very small particles upon you that I was led to the thought – for I was not sure about you – that you were skulking for some cause, and, therefore, very likely, one of my friends."

"Good God! is it possible?" he cried; as if he had been on the instant made aware of something he had not thought of before.

"Yes," said I, "it is possible and real. It is not I who am THE THIEF-CATCHER;" and as I pronounced the words I pointed my finger to the roof, and looked in the same direction, with a solemnity I really at the moment felt.

Nor was the effect less apparent upon the face of the struck youth. A tremor seemed to shake his heart, and I thought I observed a moisture in his eye, which had so often and so long no doubt been red and dry with the effects of his outlawed and dissipated life.

"Yes," he said, "there is another thief-catcher higher than you, and I feel His hand upon me with a firmer grip than that of these cuffs. I will, if God spare me, be a different man. I will confess the robbery. Yes, I will convict myself and Anderson, ay and my brother, if they and my father should murder me for it; and if you don't find me changed, my name is not Jack Ferguson."

"We may get you made a witness, and free you," said I.

"I don't want," he replied, resolutely; "I would rather be punished along with them, and, if I can get into their cells, I will try to get them to change their course of life."

This was almost the only case of penitence in a confirmed thief I ever witnessed. In the same mood, I took him up to the Office. It was afterwards arranged somehow that the devout little old man, the resetter, should be accepted as a witness, probably for the reason that he was less guilty than the others, though, in my opinion, he was the worst of the whole gang, let alone his hypocrisy, which only aggravated his resettership – a far greater crime than theft or robbery.

They were tried by the Sheriff, and got, respectively, eight, six, and four months. Whether Jack wrought out his penitential fit, I never ascertained. He got out of my beat, and I sincerely hope into another, traversed by a better angel than a detective.

The Look-Out

PEOPLE WHO BOAST of a little courage are generally very averse from the cunning that skulks and gets behind screens and defences; they can't submit to such degradation; and therefore it is that when a man is found at this kind of deceit he is set down as being a coward. I fear, however, that my courage would be pretty doubtful if it were measured in this way, for I have often enough been *perdu* in holes that would scarcely hold me, peering out for curiosities in my way, with much zest, and not at all ashamed when, bouncing out, I could catch a robber by the throat and bring him to justice.

Some sixteen years ago, Mr Tibbetts, hat-maker on the South Bridge, was greatly annoyed by that kind of disappearance of property over the counter which has no *per contra* of the appearance of cash. It is a common thing, and speaks ill for the honesty of our people as well outside as inside the counter. In this instance, the affair was a puzzle; for while Mr Tibbetts suspected his lad, there were disappearances that could not be accounted for by his dishonesty. Articles went amissing while the lad was there, but the same thing occurred when he was not there. He had tried many ways to get at the real truth, but as yet had failed, when he applied to me.

I went and examined the shop, and got all the information I could get; very unsatisfactory it was. In some views the lad seemed to be the thief, in others not; so that I saw nothing for it but a secret watch. I looked about me for a hiding place. Mr Tibbetts recommended beneath the counter, where I might hear something but see nothing. I must have a look-out, but the difficulty was where to find it in an open shop, every corner of which was known to the lad, and where any screen or artificial covering would have been suspected in a moment.

At length I fixed upon the recess behind the fanlight on the top of the door, where I could see all that took place in the shop, as well as take a look out on the street, if I chose to have a variety. Of course, I behoved to be as careful in the one direction as the other, for verily it would have been a strange thing for McLevy to have been seen doubled up behind a fanlight in a hatter's shop, waiting for a victim. To render my look-out complete, I proposed that he should surround me with bandboxes, as the milliners' apprentices are sometimes seen with on the street. The notion pleased Mr Tibbetts, and was the more acceptable, as it had often been the custom to place hat-boxes there when there was no room for them elsewhere.

Mr Tibbetts was in the practice of opening the shop in the morning himself about eight o'clock, going home to breakfast at nine, when he was relieved by the lad. To make sure work of both suppositions, – as well that implicating the lad as that applicable to outsiders, whoever they might be, – I proposed to mount into my look-out, with my bandboxes about me, as soon as the shop was opened.

Next morning at eight I was accordingly at the shop. I got up to my place by means of a ladder, and Mr Tibbetts began his part by piling up before me the bandboxes, which, as he placed them, I arranged in such a way as that I could see over the entire shop and yet not be seen by any one who had no suspicion of my being there. All things being thus prepared, we took to our respective offices; occasionally, when no customer appeared, speaking of things in general, without my feeling much of that discomfort I had awarded to so many, viz., that of a prison; myself for once being a prisoner. It is said that if every room of a house were seen into by a secret watcher, it would be a show-box even more wonderful than a travelling exhibition; and I rather think, from my experience, the remark is true.

About half past eight, a respectable-looking man, whose appearance was familiar to me, as going up and down the High Street, but whose name I did not know, came in.

"I want some hat-trimmings," said he, giving the trade description, which I did not well understand.

Mr Tibbetts shewed him some specimens of hat-trimmings; but the customer appeared to me to be very ill to please, so that the suspicion got into my mind that the man had some other object in view than to get the article wanted; nor was I wrong.

"I must go upstairs for it," said Mr Tibbetts.

"Just so," said I to myself; "and while you are upstairs, I will see what the very particular customer does."

And I did see it. No sooner was Mr Tibbetts mounted to the other storey, than the very particular customer swung himself over the counter, filled his outside pockets with trimmings – he was not now particular by any means – from a drawer; and then, vaulting over again, resumed his position.

"Ah," thinks I again, "if you just knew that McLevy is here, up in the fanlight recess, looking down upon you with these eyes!"

But he did not know it, and that was his comfort; and then, lo! all his particularity had vanished.

"Oh, just the thing."

And, after all, the quantity he bought – no doubt of an old fashion he didn't need – was so small in comparison with what he had in his big pockets, that the one, the smaller, might very well represent the amount of his real honesty; the other, the larger, standing for his assumed honesty or hypocrisy, whereby he cheated the public more effectually than he had done Mr Tibbetts.

After he had gone, I shot my head over the bandboxes.

"What is that gentleman's name, Mr Tibbetts?"

"Taylor, a small manufacturer in the Canongate, and an honest man, I believe."

"Very honest. Bring the ladder as quick as possible, and let me down."

"What do you mean? That man surely did not steal anything?"

"I'll tell you when I'm down. I never shoot secrets at people as if they were partridges."

So he got the ladder, and let me down.

"That man," said I, "is off with trimmings of at least ten times the value of what he bought off you."

"An old customer, ill to please," said he. "Ah, I see now where my goods have gone; but why did you not tell me to stop him?"

"Just because I didn't wish," said I. "He will lead us himself to the store; and, besides, it's close upon nine, and I don't wish your shopman to see me, which he might have done if there had been a protracted bustle here."

"Ah, I see," replied he.

"I wait for you on the opposite side: join me when the lad relieves you."

I took my new station, and by and by I saw the lad enter and relieve his master; who, coming out, walked on his own side towards the north. I then joined him.

"Taylor," said I, "the moment you went upstairs, sprang the counter, filled his pockets, and again took the outside, and met you as like an honest man as the most other very honest men are like themselves."

"You perfectly astonish me; though any man had sworn —"

"Yes, yes," said I.

Just the old thing, which I hear rung in my ears every day, and which I have no need to repeat; because, really, I must proceed upon the cruel and very selfish principle of taking the greater part of people for rogues until they are proved by some test honest, – not that I think honest people are fewer than others say, but just that I have somehow a difficulty in taking their own word for it.

"And where are you going?" said Mr Tibbetts.

"To Taylor's house, to which you will please take me."

"Why, I am almost ashamed to face the man," said he.

"That is a feeling I never felt," said I.

"I mean for the man," said he.

"Ah, that is another question; that feeling I have often felt, and a very painful one it is."

And so, under our necessity, we went to the house of our honest man, which we were not long in finding; neither were we long in discovering the goods. Laying my hand upon them, as they were yet warm, as it were, from the fevered hand of guilt.

"These were taken from Mr Tibbetts' shop within this half hour," said I.

The man, while betraying astonishment, did not quite lose his confidence.

"No man can say that," he replied; "these are the goods I bought from Mr Tibbetts. He went upstairs for them, and there being no one in the shop but myself, who could take it upon him to say that I stole them?"

"You don't deny it," said I; "you only assert that no one could see you."

"Yes, I deny I stole them," said he; "and, therefore, I conclude that, as there was not a single soul in the shop, you must have got your information second-hand, and that second-hand is a liar."

"How can you be certain," said I, "that no one saw you?"

"Because I have eyes," said he. "I repeat, there was no one who could by any possibility see my movements, all honest as they were, in that shop. Did you, Mr Tibbetts?"

"No, I was upstairs."

"Then I repeat, and will stand to it forever, that no one upon this earth saw me steal these trimmings."

"Upon *this earth*," said I, looking him in the face in that kind of way in which those eyes of mine, of which I am a little proud, have often enabled me to see things under the skin, and which, I am free to say, were never turned by another pair; "but there might have been one *above* who saw you."

The statement struck him, but he recovered quickly.

"Are these your goods, Mr Tibbetts?"

"Yes," said he; "I looked in my drawer," (something I have forgotten to mention,) "and found as much as these amissing."

"And, therefore," rejoined Taylor, "you fix on me, though no one saw me steal them?"

"The one *above* excepted," said I; "and by this authority I ask you to step up with me to the Police Office."

The evidence was too much for guilt, and he came

away, I taking the trimmings along with me. He was duly lodged in safe quarters, to think on the value of what he had stolen, and compare it with the worth to him of a character.

"Now, Mr Tibbetts, will this account for your losses?"

"Not at all, unless the boy has been done in the same way."

"Then I will test him, but not from above again. In the first place I can't get up, he being there; and in the second place I suspect some outside sympathisers; so I will take another position. But I will better reserve this till tomorrow morning."

"Yes," said Mr Tibbetts; "your only chance is when I am out, between nine and ten. It is now nearly ten, and he will be expecting me."

Next morning, accordingly, I was at my post at nine opposite the shop; nor did I require to wait long. I soon observed a sleazy, hawking-looking dog walking backwards and forwards, and occasionally looking in at the window. That is a resetter, said I to myself; for I have a knowledge of the tribe, always cowardly and side-looking, never with the firm defiant eye of a confirmed thief.

Thus watching my man, I saw him slip suddenly into the passage of the common stair to the south of the shop. What next? Almost what I expected, – the lad came to the door, looked north and south, and round and round, then, going to the common stair, peered in. Ah, everywhere, thought I, but right opposite, where I *am*. So it is always, when people wish to do something wrong; they look about for danger, which they don't wish to find, and therefore they never look in the proper direction. If they did, they would seldom do the evil thing, for, though the danger is not *patent*, it may always be seen, if the wish were away and the eye left to the guidance of honesty and wisdom. Although I was not known to him, he might have looked into the drawer whence he was to abstract what he abstracted, and then consider that his master could not but miss his goods. That was his proper direction, but he looked out in place of within.

In a minute after, he came to the door again, with a bundle behind him, looked about again, – what trouble vice puts itself to under the aspect of prudence! – and darted into the entry. A clever enough trick, as he thought, but then I had a motive for dashing in as strong as his, and I obeyed it. Hastening over the street, I was in upon them just as the lad had handed the bundle to the resetter.

"What is this?" said I, laying hold of it.

"Some clothes of the boy," said the man, "which I have got for my wife to wash for him."

"And your wife washes span new hat-trimmings?" said I, pulling out an end.

The usual dashed and blank looks of those who are catched red-handed.

I took them both direct to the Office, where Taylor was before them, though the parties were in no way connected. As for the man, I felt nothing. I had sympathy for the boy, who in all likelihood was led into this breach of trust by the older culprit. The law makes allowance for the authority exercised by a husband over a wife, whereby she is often freed, while the real truth is that the authority is often reversed; but there is no allowance for that cunning persuasion exercised by full-grown men over mere striplings – a very deadly thing, and I am satisfied very common. The father and mother of a thief, who have trained him from youth upwards to the habit, get clear because they didn't do the deed, and the wretched pupil is made the scapegoat of their sins. I have seen hundreds of boys and girls convicted and sentenced who had, considering their years and education, no more moral guilt on their heads than the unfortunate cat bore while under the hand of the monkey. So in this case the lad and the man got sixty days each; but it was just a wonder that the latter was punished at all, for if he had not been caught in the act, he might not have been discovered without a difficulty not applicable to the thief himself.

The time apportioned to Taylor scarcely repaid his crime. But Mr Tibbetts' evils were all cured in twenty-four hours. I never heard more of his being exposed to robberies of trimmings or anything else.

The Pirates

ALMOST EVERY CASE which has come into my hands, and in which there was difficulty in tracing, has had something to mark it as demanding a treatment suited to its peculiarity. In following that treatment, I have had occasion, in conformity to the latitude intrusted to me, to differ from my colleagues, but seldom with much cause to repent of my pertinacity. In the case I am now to narrate, this occurred to a greater extent than in some others; and, perhaps, it is on that account – for the transaction itself is of frequent occurrence, the robbery of a tar – that I recur to it.

In 1845, we were called upon by a sailor of the name of Geddes, a Newhaven man. He was in that state in which these good-natured fellows often are, after having passed a night in some of the low houses, in the midst of half-a-dozen of depraved women, collected around him by the attraction of a bunch of notes. He came in very unsteady, and withal jolly, with the indispensable quid in his mouth, and the hitching up the breeches as usual. I asked him his errand.

"Why, you see," said he, "I was boarded and robbed

by a nest of pirates over in that creek there," pointing towards the other side of the High Street.

"When?" said I.

"Last night, second watch."

"A very loose watch, I fear," said I. "Why didn't you keep a better look-out?"

"Right, sir; but then you see we had too much grog, and got hazy about the eyes, so that we couldn't see the enemy nohow, until fairly boarded, and now it's all up with my cargo."

"What had you on you? Have you been at sea?"

"Why, yes, your honour, I had been cruising in the South Sea, and came to Leith yesterday, where I laid in a cargo of notes, twenty-eight of 'em, and wanted to have a scour among the fire-ships up in this danger-ous sea, and so got robbed you see; everything gone, sir, – not a penny – nothing left, but this piece of seal-skin, with an inch or two of pigtail."

"You have paid for your fun," said I; "but where did this happen?"

"I think the name of the creek," he went on, "is Galloway's Close. The captain in charge of the pirates, Hill, or something of that shape. Then there was Nell, Grace, Moll, and Agnes; but I couldn't tell one from t'other now."

"But why didn't you take care of your hard-won money, man?"

"And so I did, – lockers bolted and barred; but they silenced me with their charges of gin and whisky, and when I went to sleep, scrambled up the sides of my craft, and robbed me of every penny. So if you can't make sail and catch 'em, I must off again to sea; but catch me next time, – I'll give that creek a wide berth, or my name's not Jack Geddes."

"Can you tell me what like the women were?"

"All of a piece to my eyes – just women, every one of them, that's all; all the same you know when a man's groggy; but I wouldn't mind it so much if they hadn't sheered off, and left me a disabled hulk, without a biscuit in the locker, and nothing to comfort me, but a sore head and two quids or so."

"You have mentioned four names; do you remember any more?" said I.

"No, can't say, – half-a-dozen anyhow."

"Why had you so many sweethearts?"

"Oh, we like a choice you know," said he, laughing; "at first there were only Nell and Molly, then one told t'other as how I had a rich cargo, and so the fleet collected."

"Well, I'll try what can be done for you," said I.

"I hope you'll give 'em a taste of the grating and cat anyhow."

"Wouldn't it be of more importance if I could get the money?"

"Oh yes; wouldn't require to go to sea again; and then mother would get something, you know, and old father."

"If you had given it to them to keep," said I, "you wouldn't have been here today."

"Yes," he replied, with a comic kind of seriousness

stealing over his face, if there was not something like a drop gathering in his eye, of which I was the more certain that he brought the sleeve of his jacket over his forehead. "Yes; the old ones will get nothing till next time, and I'd rather not see 'em till I've gone to sea again, and come home and make 'em happy. I'll keep out of Galloway's Creek next bout, I warrant."

"Would you know them if you saw them?"

"Wouldn't I know the cut of the enemy?" said he, getting into his old humour. "They came too close quarters for my not knowing 'em."

"But you cannot tell which of them took the money?"

"No; I just remember a low room, stoups and glasses, and a fleet of women. I was singing 'Tom Bowling', and Nell was helping me, – others singing something else, and one or two dancing, – all merry and jolly, – when I must have fallen asleep, for the next thing I remember was that they were all off, the gas out, and nothing to be seen but darkness – and all my money gone; nothing but the seal-skin pouch and the quid to go to sea with again."

"It's a hard case, my lad," said I; "but you have brought it upon yourself by your folly. I'm sure you all know well enough of these tricks, and yet they are always coming fresh upon us. I will set about trying to get hold of the pirates, as well as your money. Call back in the afternoon, and in the meantime keep a look-out about the streets, and endeavour to lay hold of them."

So away he went, hitching in the old style. I had no great hopes of his case. The women he had mentioned were known to me very well, as residing in, or frequenters of, a Mrs Hill's establishment, in the close he had mentioned; but they were experienced hands, and so well up to "planking" such an easily disposed of article as money in the shape of banknotes, that to get hold of the thieves was making scarcely any progress. But the difference I have alluded to was as regards the first step. Going direct to the den is often held to be the best method of getting hold of a beast who is glutted with prey; but women, even of their depraved kind, are not exactly beasts, though in many respects worse. They are not altogether deprived of the glimmer of reason sufficient to tell them that their lair will be the first searched. To go there is simply to give them warning, and put them on their guard. Yet this is the common way of many detectives; and I was only taking my old way when I insisted, against a contrary opinion, that we must in the first place avoid the house.

But there is another consideration, derived from the inevitable nature of women. The moment they get hold of more money than will serve them for their always crying immediate wants, including the eternal whisky, their very first thought is dress. They will go a-shopping at all hazards. Their trade is to attract, and it often enough happens that the very shawl, or bonnet, or gown which helps to ensnare the victim, is the produce of a robbery similar to that they will practise upon him; so that, I believe, it has occurred that, as the money is distributed from one to another, a man has been caught and robbed by means of the cash he had in his pocket a night or two before. There is a pretty bit of redistribution here, very instructive; but I believe it's all one whether understood and felt or not. If sin were to be cured by the scab of its own cautery, it would have been off the face of the earth some thousands of years ago, down to the pit, never to be allowed to come up again to taint this fair world.

Proceeding upon my theory of avoiding the house, I, accompanied by one or two constables, betook myself to the Bridges, where are the shops most frequented by women of this stamp. I just wanted to know if the thieves were true to their old nature. They had had time enough to sleep off the effects of the whisky, and to awake to little else than the madness of their conviction that they had each a bundle of notes in their pockets, which it was necessary they should scatter, by purchasing new things, to enable them to get quit of the old rags.

I accordingly kept pacing the Bridges, as if in no hurry consequent upon the sailor's story; and I believe if they had seen me, they would have been satisfied either that Jack was still in Mrs Hill's, or that he had never been to the Office. On the other hand, if I had seen *them*, I could have read money in their eyes. Yes, as I have hinted before, if you know the general cast of the features of people who live from hand to mouth, – and a very artful hand sometimes, in the case of that class over whom I exercise a fatherly care, – you can almost with certainty tell whether any windfall has come in their way, for you may be assured that nothing but money can make them look happy; and then the happiness has a kind of hysterical excitement about it that carries a mark to a good observer. Nay, when a good haul is got of £20 to £100, there is often observed a commotion in the whole sisterhood, even among those who don't participate in the plunder, for doesn't it shew that there are prizes in their lottery? Their fortunate turn will come next; the victims are getting rich and unwary; – and, above all, there is the inevitable envy of the lucky sister or sisters who have been so unspeakably fortunate, without taking into account that there will be drink going in the "happy lands" for a week to come, until the money is all spent and gone.

After keeping up my watch for more than an hour, I observed Helen Mossman and Grace Edwards coming out of a respectable shop, each with a neatly tied up draper's bundle. I kept my eye upon them. They had the happiness of shopping in their hearts, and were babbling, as money-holders do; nor did they seem to have any fear of being laid hold of, though, of course, they did not see me. In the midst of their talk, they met Agnes Pringle and Mary Cameron bouncing out of another shop, where they also had been getting their neat paper parcels, and then they commenced a quadruple conversation, apparently extremely interesting to them, for they laughed heartily, and even, you would have thought, turned their eyes contemptuously on the passengers on either side of them, as if they said to themselves, "We have been shopping as well as the best of you;" for to what woman is the pride, let alone the pleasure, of shopping not dear? But as I stood and watched them, another thought occurred to me. There stood four women, who had taken from a poor seaman the wages of a year's voyage to the other side of the world, and left him not so much as would get him a day's tobacco, while he had an old father and an old mother looking to him for help, and only to be met with the miserable intelligence that their hopes were blasted. What did this poor fellow do to them that they should render him penniless, even make his stout heart swell with pity for these parents, and bring the tear to his eye, to be brushed off in shame of what he thought his weakness? No, they cared nothing for these things. Jack was not even mentioned, only collars, and ribbons, and handkerchiefs, to deck them out for some other seduction.

I was in no hurry. Here I had Jack's Nell, and Moll, and Grace, and Agnes, all in a neat clump, while, if I had taken the advice given to me, I might not have had one of them; for a visit to Galloway Creek would have sent Sarah Hill, the daughter of the keeper of the house, out upon a hunt, after them, to tell them to keep out of the way; and this they might have done till every penny of the £28 was gone. My men were now behind me, for they had also seen the birds getting into the net; so, stepping up to them, –

"You are blocking up the way, my ladies; walk on."

"Walk to the devil!" said Nell Mossman. "The street is not yours."

"We will walk any way we please," said another.

"Which way do you want us to walk?" said a third.

"This way," said I, pointing north; "this way, come along."

And so they did; for in spite of their bravery they began to get alarmed.

I walked along with them to the Tron.

"Oh, not that way," stopping them as they moved for the Canongate; "this way, past the Tron."

"And why that way?"

"Never mind, come along, and here is a friend who will go with us and bear us company;" and who's this but Jack, all sober and tidy, with a clean light at his poop and a fine breeze in his main-sheet?

"All right," he cried, as he came up; "direct for port, four passengers and a valuable cargo."

And Jack came to my side, as the cowed and heartless creatures still kept mechanically trudging by our side.

"Old mother and father have a chance yet," said I, in a low tone to the tar.

"Oh, God bless you, sir," rejoined he; "were it not for them I wouldn't have cared a d—n, but since ever I saw you this morning my heart has been thumping against my ribs, like a moored lugger against the wooden fenders of a pier, all for the thought of the old ones."

And there the drop came again.

"D'ye know, sir," he continued, "I had made up my mind ..."

"For what?"

"Not to see 'em after eighteen months' absence, but just away to the West Indies again today."

"This way, ladies," said I, as we came to our haven.

And as they turned and stood for a moment in hesitation, though they had seen plainly enough for several minutes whither they were bound, Jack stood and surveyed his jolly friends of the preceding night's revelry and madness. There was a good-natured triumph in his clear eye.

"Why," cried he, with an oath, "this is so jolly good a thing, I'd have the same fight again to have these land-pirates at my stern."

"Step in."

And thus I had the entire company within my harbour; and then we began to unload the outlaws, an officer being sent to the house to search it. A part was found there, and the rest had been pretty fairly distributed, so that, making allowance for the purchases and a few drams, we got, one way and another, almost the whole of Jack's £28. Thus old father and mother would have a chance, after all, of getting a few comforts through the mean of their good-hearted son. Yet, I believe, the most curious and lamentable feature of this case is that to which I have partially alluded, – the utter want in these women of anything like a sense that they had done anything that was wrong in reducing *a poor man* to beggary. It is nothing to see them hardened in cases where the victims are rich, – the "serve-em-well" doctrine applies there with perhaps a touch of retribution, for such women are in that predicament from the selfish licentiousness and hollow-hearted deceit of rich seducers.

Nor, do I believe, did they feel more when, tried by the Sheriff and a jury, they got their rewards: Helen Mossman twelve months, Grace Edwards six, Agnes Pringle and Mary Cameron nine, and Sarah Hill, the bawd's daughter, as resetter, seven. "The pirates' doom."

The Sea Captain

I DOUBT WHETHER the good philanthropical people are even yet quite up to all the advantages of ragged schools. The salvation of society from a host of harpies is not the main chance; neither is it that the poor wretches are sold into the slavery of vice and misery before they know right from wrong. There's something more. I have a suspicion that society loses often what might become its sharpest and most intelligent members in these half-starved youngsters, whose first putting out of the hand is the beginning of a battle with the world. I'm not to try to account for the fact, but I am pretty well satisfied, from all I have seen, that the children of these poor half-starved people are something more apt than the sons of your gentlemen. You who are learned may try your hand at the paradox, and make as much of it as you do of the other riddles of human life. Here is a plea for the John Poundses and Dr Guthries, of which they could make something. Every ragged urchin they lay hold of to make him learn from books has been at a school of another kind, where he has got his energies sharpened on a different whetstone from that found within a school, and then the school does its duty in directing these energies.

Just fancy what some of our card-sharpers would have been if their cleverness had been directed towards honest and lawful undertakings. I have known some of these gentlemen so adroit at the great problem of ways and means that they might have shone as Chancellors of the Exchequer. It is not their fault that we find them out. Their great drawback is, that they begin to be cunning and adroit before they know the world. All this close cunning defeats itself. The young rogues put me often in mind of moles. They work in dark holes, but they are always coming near the surface, where they hitch up friable hillocks to let air in, and so are caught. Nay, they sometimes hitch themselves out into the midday sun of justice. I have at this moment two or three of these misdirected geniuses in my eye whom I have traced from early childhood – aye that period when the Raggedier officers should have laid hold of them.

In April 1854, an honest joiner in Banff of the name of Donald McBeath, had taken it into his head that he would do well to go to England, where his talents would be appreciated. In short, Donald had working within him the instinct of that little insect so familiar to the Highlanders, the tendency of which is to go south – probably because it knows in some inscrutable way that Englishmen have thick blood. Then he had friends in Newcastle who had gone before him, and found out that the yellow blood corpuscles of the social body flowed there more plentifully than in Banff. Were I to be more fanciful, I would say that Donald McBeath had the second sight – for money. He loved it so well that he had stomach for "ta hail Pank of England", and would "maype return in ta grand coach and ta grey horses." Nor had this love been as yet without fruits, for he had by Highland penury saved no less a sum than seven pounds, all stowed away in a sealskin spleuchan, besides seven more which he had laid out on a capital silver watch – convinced that no Highland shentleman bearing a royal name, as he did, could pass muster in England without this commodity.

The Highlanders were never at any time in the habit of getting lighter or leaner by moving from one place to another, if they were not generally a good deal heavier at the end of their journey than at the beginning. So true to the genius of his race, he laid his plans so that, in progressing south, he would lay contributions on his "friends" all the way, in order that, if it "could be possible," he might keep the seven pounds all entire – some extra shillings being provided for the voyage in the *Britannia* from Leith to Newcastle. How many Highland cousins suffered during this transport of the valuable person of the King's clansman till he got to Leith, I never had any means of knowing. We cannot be far wrong, however, in supposing that he shook them all heartily by the hand; and no pedigree of the McFarlans from Parlan downwards, was ever courted with more industry than that of the McBeaths, if it was possible to bring within the tree any collateral branch with McBeath blood in his veins, meal in his girnal, and a bed fit for a Highlander. Then the shake of the hand, and the "oigh, oigh" of true happiness, were the gratitude which is paid beforehand – the only kind that Donald knew anything of; or any other body I suspect – at least if I can judge from what I have received from so many to whom I have given lodgings, meat, and free passages.

Arrived at Leith, the first thing Donald did was to get out the little bit of snuff-coloured paper which contained the names of the cousins, and where, among the rest, was that of an old woman in the Kirkgate who was a descendant of the sister of Donald's grandmother, a McNab, – as unconscious of being related to the clan of the murderous king as anyone could be, before such a flood of light was cast upon her history as Donald was well able to shed. He soon found her out; and though Janet McNab could make nothing of the pedigree, she could count feelings of humanity; and what was more, she had a supper and a bed to save an infraction upon the said seven pounds.

Next morning, after having partaken of a Highland breakfast from poor Janet, which could only be calculated by the professions of eternal friendship uttered by a Gael, Donald went forth to see the craft which in some cheap berth was to transport him to the land of gold; and, to be sure, it was not long till he saw the vessel lying alongside of the quay. No doubt she was to be honoured in her freight. It was not every day the *Britannia* carried a McBeath with seven pounds in his pocket, a seven pound watch in his fob, and a chest of tools, which was to cut his way to fortune. Then if it were just possible that the captain had ever been in Banff, or had in his veins a drop of Celtic blood – he would ascertain that by and by, he might even be a McBeath or a McNab.

Much, however, as he expected from the clanship of the captain of the *Britannia*, who was not then to be seen, he had sense enough to know that that officer could not abate his passage-money. Nay, he knew that he must take out his ticket at the office on the shore, and thither he accordingly hied to make a bargain. Unfortunately these tickets are not liable to be affected by Highland prigging; but the loose shillings to which I have alluded allowed him still to retain untouched the seven pounds. Yea, that seven pounds seemed to have a charmed life, the charm being only to be broken by same such wonder as the march of some wood or forest from one part of the kingdom to the other, or by the man who should try to take it having been from the belly of a shark "untimely ript".

It wanted still some considerable time until the *Britannia* sailed, and Donald thought that he might as well get his chest of tools and bag of clothes put on board. He accordingly hied away to Mrs McNab's, and having returned his thanks for her kindness, if he did not promise her a part of his fortune "when it should be made," he got the packets on his broad shoulders, and proceeded to the vessel. He was more lucky this time. A seaman, very probably the captain, was busy walking the deck.

"Hallo, tare!" cried Donald to the seaman, "you'll be ta captain?"

"Yes, all right," replied the other; "and you'll be a passenger for Newcastle; what have you got there?"

"My tool chest and clothes," replied Donald; "fery valuable, cost seven pounds ten shillings."

"Heave them along the gunwale there," said the seaman, "they can be stowed away afterwards; but you're too soon, we won't heave off for an hour."

"Ower sune is easy mended," replied the Gael.

"And sometimes," in a jolly way, said the other, "we have time for a dram."

"Ay, and inclination maype too," cried Donald, quite happy.

"Come away, then, our lockers are shut, so we'll have it up the way, where I know they keep the real peat-reek, and I'll pay."

And Donald, leaving his luggage, but carrying with him a notion that the captain of the *Britannia* deserved to be one other Majesty's Admirals of the Blue, followed his guide until they entered the house of the publican, whose name I do not at present recollect. Nor was this notion in any way modified even when they were seated at the same table with three very respectable-looking men, apparently engaged in the harmless pastime of playing at cards. Nay, the notion was evidently shared by the three strangers, who, although they had clearly never seen the captain of the *Britannia* before, offered him, with a generosity wonderful to Donald, a share of their liquor. On his side, the generosity was equalled by his insisting that they, whom he declared he had never seen before, should take a part of his. Never was there such generous unanimity among strangers; and even Donald was included in the newborn friendship. Then the harmless play went on. There were only three cards used, two diamonds and one clubs; and the game was so simple that the Gael understood it in a moment, for it consisted in a little shuffling, and if one drew the clubs, he was the winner of the stakes. The generous captain laid down a stake of a pound; one of the players laid down another; then the cards were shuffled in so obvious a manner that a child might have seen where the clubs lay; and so to be sure the captain saw what a child might have seen, drew the slip, and pocketed the two pounds. This was repeated, until the captain pocketed six pounds; and Donald seeing fortune beckoning on, tabled one of the seven with the charmed unity. None of these men had been cut out of the belly of a shark, and so Donald McBeath's seven was made eight.

"Play on," whispered the captain, "while I go to look after your luggage."

And so to be sure the Highlander did. He staked pound after pound, gained once in thrice, got furious, and staked on and on till the seven was nil.

Then rose the Highlander's revenge; the watch was tabled against seven pounds, and went at a sweep.

"And now, py Cot, to croon a', ya *Pritannia* will be gone," he cried, as he rushed out in agony.

Frantic as he was, he could yet find his way to the part of the pier where he expected to see the vessel with the noble captain on board. The steamer was gone; and as he stood transfixed in despair, a man came up to him.

"Was it you who carried some luggage on board the *Britannia* about an hour ago?"

"Ay, just me."

"Well, then, I saw a man dressed in seaman's clothes carry it away. He seemed to make for Edinburgh, likely by the Easter Road."

"And whaur is ta Easter Road?" cried the Gael, as he turned round to run in some direction, though in what he knew not.

At length, after many inquiries, he got into the said road, and hurrying along at the top of his speed, he expected every moment to see the captain. He questioned every one he met, got no trace, and began to lose hope with breath; for, long ere this, he had seen the full scope of his folly, and suspected that the captain was one of the card-sharpers. Fairly worn out, – more the consequence of the excited play of his lungs and galloping blood than the effect of his chase, – he slackened his pace when he came to the Canongate. There he was – a ruined man, not a penny left, the hopes of a fortune blasted, even his tool-chest, with which he might have cut his way anywhere, gone, – a terrible condition, no doubt, not to be even conceived properly by those who have not experienced the shock of sudden and total ruin. No sight had any interest for him, no face any beauty or ugliness, except as it carried any feature like what he recollected of his cruel and heartless companions. Nor was he free from self-impeachment, blaming his love of money as well as the blindness of his credulity. While in this humour, and making his way by inquiry to the Police Office, he met right in the face, and seemed to spring up three inches as he detected the features of one of his spoilers. In an instant, his hand clutched, with the tension of a tiger's muscle, the gasping throat of the villain. The Highland blood was boiling, and you might have seen the red glare of his eye, as if all his revenge for what he considered to be the ruin of a life had been concentrated in that one terrible glance. The sharper, strong, and with all the recklessness of a tribe of the most desperate kind, was only as a sapling in his grasp. "My money and my watch, you tarn villain!" Words which, accompanied by the contortion of Gaelic gesticulation, only brought about him a crowd, among whom two constables made their appearance. The sharper was transferred to their hands, glad enough to be relieved of his more furious antagonist, and all the three made for the Office.

It was at this part of the strange drama I came into play. The moment I saw the Highlander enter with his man, I suspected the nature of the complaint, for I knew he was from the country, and the sharper, David Wallace, was one of my most respected *protégés* in the card and thimble-rigging line; but I required the information given me by the Highlander to make me understand all the dexterity of the trick which the pseudo-captain of the *Britannia* had practised. The club, I knew, consisted of four, David Wallace, Richard Kyles, John Dewar, and John Sweeny. It was regularly organised, each man having attached to him his gillet of a helpmate, ready to secrete or carry the watches and other property won by their lords at this most unequal game. I have always considered those daylight sharpers, who, without instruments other than three cards or three thimbles and a pea, contrive to levy extensive contributions on society, as men worthy to have been drawn into the ranks of honest citizens, where their talents could not have failed to elevate them into wealth. Even the manipulation of these simple instruments is more wonderful than the tricks of a conjurer. Fix your eyes as you may, be suspicious even to certainty that the player is cheating you, I will defy you to detect the moment when, by the light if not elegant touch of the finger, your pea has been slipped from the right thimble to the wrong, or the right card to the wrong – yea, to the end, you could swear that no deception has been or could be practised upon you; and even when your watch is forfeited you could hardly think but that your misfortune lay on some defect in your power of penetration. And so it does. You are cheated – nay, *fairly cheated*. You can't expect from such men that they should undertake not to deceive you. If they had no art, you would ruin them in five minutes, for all you would have to do (and you insist on the unfair privilege) is to watch the thimble under which your fortune lies and snatch it. There is, therefore, no pity due to the victims of these men's deceptions, and this we can say with a thorough condemnation of the men themselves.

As soon as I understood the transaction, it was my duty to detect the right thimble, and I had no fear of deception. I sent Wallace, under charge of a constable, to the Leith Office, and told McBeath that I would have the three others there in the course of a couple of hours. I had no doubt that Dewar, the cleverest of them, had personated the captain, and that he had rejoined his associates to share the booty. I knew their haunt, a public house in Bristo Street, and, taking Riley with me, I went direct to the place. My luck was nothing less than wonderful. Just as I entered I met my three men coming out of a room, and holding out my arms –

"Stop, gentlemen," said I; "I have got something to say to you."

But I didn't need to say it. They understood me as well as I did them.

"Captain Dewar of the *Britannia*," said I, looking to Dewar.

"At your service," replied the rogue, with a spice of humour, at which, in the very midst of their choking wrath, they could not help leering.

Well, the old process. "Search," said I; "I want seven pounds and a watch."

And calling in my assistant, I began my search. No resistance. They were too well up to their calling.

I found the watch on Wallace. No more. The pounds had been given to the fancies.

I kept my word by having them all three at Leith within a couple of hours, safely lodged in prison. They were afterwards tried by the Leith magistrates, aided by an assessor, and sentenced to sixty days each, with sixty more if they did not give up the money and luggage. The sentence seemed judicious, and in one sense it was; but the worthy bailies did not consider that they were offering a premium on the seductive and depredating energies of the trulls, who (long after the seven pounds was spent) in order to get their birds out of the cage, set about their arts and redeemed them from bondage.

The Society-Box

THE WAY BY WHICH the ranks of thieves and robbers are recruited is by the *old* teaching the *young* the figure system. Yes, there is a proselytism of evil as well as of good. Society is always straining after the making of parties, and while churches are working for members, the old thieves are busy enlisting the young. The advantage, I fear, is with the latter, for there's something more catching in the example of taking another man's property than that of praying for grace. Of course I am here looking to the young, and I make this statement without caring much how your beetle-browed critic may take it.

I have known a good many of those dominies of the devil's lore, not a few of them with streaks of grey on their heads, who, having themselves been taught at the same desk, have taken up the trade as a kind of natural calling, and raised their pupils according to the old morality, "The sweet morsel of another person's property is pleasant to roll under the tongue;" and perhaps the more pleasant, too, that the tongue that *sucks* is the tongue that *lies*. There was Hugh Thomson, about the cleverest thief in my day, that rogue brought up as many youngsters in the faith as would have filled a conventicle; and what a glorious grip that was I got of him, just as he was trying to reap the fruits of his lesson, through the ingenuity of one of his scholars, William Lang! I would not have exchanged it for the touch of a bride's hand, with the marriage ring upon her finger.

In 1841, there was a Mr Brown who kept a spirit shop in the Low Calton, nearly opposite Trinity College Church. One of those modern unions called "Yearly Societies" was kept in his house, the members paying their contributions on the Monday evenings, which contributions, the produce of toil and sweat of poor, hard-working men, were deposited in the society-box, and secured under lock and key. One Monday evening I was passing down the Calton on my way to Leith Wynd homeward, to get myself refreshed with a cup of tea. In the mouth of an entry, on the other side of the street called the North Back of the Canongate, I observed Hugh and his scholar Lang, engaged, no doubt, in the mutual offices of teaching and learning. I thought I might learn something too, and stepping into the recess of Trinity Church gate, I watched their movements. Shortly, Lang came out – he had become a man by this time, recollect – and having mixed with the workmen, who were going into Brown's shop to make their weekly payments, he went in among the rest.

At first, I confess, I could not understand this. The thief could make nothing of the workmen, even if unknown to them as a thief, which in all likelihood he was, and the idea of his trying the pocket line among fustian jackets never entered my head. But that there was some play to go on, where Thomson was patronising, I could have no doubt whatever. After a time, during which I took care that Thomson should not see me, Lang came out, and, having joined Thomson, the two went off together, with something that sounded in my ears as a laugh, and the meaning of which was made clear to me by a happy thought that occurred to me on the instant like a flash. I now wanted to see Brown by himself, but as the workmen were still going in and coming out, I was obliged to wait a considerable time. Selecting at length a moment when the coast was tolerably clear, I entered the shop. There, in the back room, was the sacred box, devoted to benevolence, and from which some widow and orphans might, before the year expired, receive something that would make *her* tear less scorching and *their* cry less shrill – some broken bones, too, broken through the labour and toil of the poor man for the rich one, might have less pain through the charm of that box. Thoughts these pretty enough to some minds, but to such as Thomson quaint, if not funny.

"Mr Brown," said I, as I entered, "will you be kind enough to shew me your list of members?"

"Surely, Mr McLevy." And he placed the book in my hands.

Running down the names I came to "William Lang, joiner," though all his *junctions* were between his hand and the property of another.

"I have seen enough," said I; "and now, Mr Brown, you will take especial care to carry your box upstairs with you tonight to your dwelling-house."

And without giving him time to ask for explanations, which I did not feel much disposed to give, I left him. I knew that Brown shut up late on the pay-nights, and therefore having plenty of time that evening, even in the event of an emergency, I went home to get my tea. After which, and having cogitated a little under its reviving influence, I took another turn down Leith Wynd. I wanted to examine the iron gate leading to the church. On looking at it, I found that the lock was off, and consequently free ingress was afforded to anyone wishing to enter. I went to a blacksmith's and got a chain and padlock, the use of which will be apparent, when I mention, that if I adopted the recess within the gate as a look-out, from which I could see Brown's shop, it was as likely to be so used by those we wanted to observe, as by ourselves, the observers.

Having made these preliminary arrangements, I proceeded to the Office, where I secured the services of one or two of the most active constables, besides my assistant, for I knew that having Thomson to cope with, we had something to encounter far more formidable than any other thief or robber within the sound of St Giles's. I was in all this, I admit, fired with the ambition of getting a man who had become as bold as Macbeth under the witches' prophecy. Having waited till about eleven o'clock, the hour when Brown generally closed, I repaired, accompanied by my men, to our place of retreat. We entered cautiously, and shutting the old gate with as little noise as possible, I secured the two halves with the chain and padlock, with which I had provided myself – a proceeding which, as it afterwards appeared, was necessary to the success of our enterprise, but the object of which my men could not at the time very clearly understand. Yet what more likely than that Thomson and his gang should wish to reconnoitre us, as we wished to reconnoitre them. We were soon enclosed, and ready for observation. We saw the light put out in Brown's shop, and heard the locking of the doors both in front and at the back, or rather in the side of the entry which led up to the premises above which the spirit-dealer resided. But more than this, we saw the cautious cashier with the sacred box under his arm, as he stept up the entry – a sight which I enjoyed with a secret chuckle of satisfaction, for it was no mean pride to be up with a man such as Hugh Thomson.

It might be about twelve o'clock before we saw any symptoms of sport. Suddenly, three men, coming apparently from different directions, met, and whispering a few words parted, to act for caution-scouts to each other. Each took a round, casting wary glances to the right and left, and desultory as their movements were, I could recognise Hugh, Lang, and another, David L——, also an old pupil of Thomson's. It seemed to be Thomson's special care to look into the Trinity Church recess, and as we saw him coming forward, we retreated behind the pillars of the gate.

He appeared to be taken aback as he observed the gate secured, and taking hold of a railing, he shook it; so that it was evident to me that the place we occupied had been fixed on for retreat, if not for observation. I had thus again the advantage of my old friend, and the moment he receded we resumed our posts. In a few minutes, the different scouts seemed to agree in the opinion that all was safe, and went direct to the work I had anticipated, the moment I saw Lang enter with the members of the society. The front door was not their object; it was the back, or more properly the side one in the entry, which, from the passage being right opposite to us, I could see along, though very indistinctly, scarcely more than to enable me to trace their dark figures against the light thrown in at the farthest opening. None but a keen trapper or snarer can appreciate the pleasure a detective of the true instinctive order feels when engaged in the capture of game so wild, shy, and cunning. Their very cunning is what whets our appetites, and I absolutely burned to embrace the dauntless leader of the gang.

Now we saw one separate from the rest, come up the entry, and begin to act the "goose-guard", dodging backwards and forwards, throwing up his head, and looking from one side to another. Inside the entry, meanwhile, some obstruction seemed to take place, even adroit as Thomson was; but presently we were surprised as a vivid flash of exploded gun-powder illuminated the passage. Though unprepared for this, I understood it at once. Thomson had a way of his own with *sullen* locks – placing a small parcel of powder into the keyhole, and pushing it home, so as to reach the wards, he exploded it with a match. The only thing I wondered at was the scarcely audible report – perhaps to be accounted for by the moderate charge, and the resistance of the guards which he intended to loosen. So long as they were in the entry, we could not move, even to undo the padlock and get the gate open and ready. Our moment was that of their entrance; and watching thus, with breathless anxiety, we saw that the door had been opened, by the disappearance of the shadows from the entry. Out we sallied. The "goose-guard", L——, is made secure in an instant. Two constables, placed one on each side of the front door. I and my assistant enter the close and get to the side door. Lo! it is locked. The gentlemen had wanted time, not only to rifle the box, but to enjoy themselves with ample potations from the whisky barrel; and no doubt their libations would have been rather costly to Mr Brown, as every minute besides would have been devoted to the abstraction of as many portables as they could carry away.

Finding the door barred, (for I think the lock must have been rendered useless,) we began to force it – a circumstance that really added to my satisfaction, as every wrench and thump must have gone home to the hearts of the intruders, now fairly caught in a novel man-trap. Nay, with the constables at the outer door, I didn't care what noise we made, provided we were not annoyed by curious neighbours; and then, to make the play more exciting, we heard them as busy with the

front door trying to get *out*, as we were with the back
one endeavouring to get *in*. Forced at length, and a rush
in in the dark, the noise making the thieves desperate,
so that their energies to force the front door might
rather be termed fury. They succeeded, just as we were
at their back; and in consequence of the door being
in two halves, and one starting open while the constables' eyes were fixed on the other, Lang bolted, at the
moment that Thomson was embraced by a powerful
constable. Another constable was off immediately in
pursuit of Lang; and such was my weakness, that when
I saw Thomson struggling ineffectually in the grasp
of the officer, one whom I had so often sighed for in
secret, and eyed in openness, that I took him from the
man with that kind of feeling that no person ought to
have the honour of holding him but myself.

By this time Mr Brown was down among us in great
consternation.

"Ah!" said he, "I see the reason now of your having
told me to carry the society-box upstairs."

"I fear that would have been nothing to your loss,"
replied I, "if we hadn't been as sharp as we have been.
All's right."

Mr Brown's fears were appeased, and we then
marched our gentlemen up to the Office, in which
procession, so honoured by the presence of Hugh
Thomson, I enjoyed one of my triumphs. Lang was
sought for during weeks, but could not be found; and
here I have to recount one of my wonders. One dark
evening when I was acting the night-hawk out near

the Gibbet Toll, I had gone considerably beyond that mark, and was returning. Dalkeith is a kind of harbour of refuge for the Edinburgh thieves when the city becomes too hot for them, and I had some hopes of an adventure on this road, otherwise I would not have been there at that hour, for it was late. The road to Portobello is also a hopeful place at times; but on that night I had some reasons, known only to myself, (and it was not often surmised where I was at any time,) for preferring the southern opening. Well, sauntering along I met a young fellow, but it was so dark that, at the distance of two or three yards, you could scarcely recognise anybody. I had a question ready, however, that suited all comers.

"Am I right for the city?" said I.

"Right in," was the reply.

And seeing the man wanted to be off, I darted a look at the side of his face. It was Lang's; and I suspected he had recognised *me* before I did *him*, for he was off in an instant on the way to Dalkeith, and I must take to my heels in pursuit, or lose him. I immediately gave chase, and a noble one it was, though the night was as dark as pitch, and every step was through liquid mud.

Lang was a good runner, and had, I fancy, confidence that he would escape, and that which he had to escape from might very well grease the heels of even a lazy fellow. He ran for freedom, that dear treasure of even a thief's soul; and I ran to deprive him of it, a feeling as dear to a detective. The race became hot and hotter, and I could see only the dark outline of the flying desperado, and I heard the sound of his rapid steps as the voice of hope. By the side of the road one or two people stood, and seemed to wonder at the chase, but no one ventured to interfere. We had run a mile and a half with no abatement of the speed of either, so that we were about equal, and if this continued we might run to Dalkeith; but this issue was rendered improbable by the fact, quite well known to me, that a *pursued criminal,* with a clever officer after him, may almost always be caught by loss of breath. The impulse under which he flies is far more trying to the nerves than that which impels the officer to follow, and hence it is that criminals are so often what is called "run down". The same remark is applicable to a chase of animals. Fear eats up the energies, the lungs play violently, and exhaustion is the consequence. And so it was here. I gained as time sped, and at length I heard the grateful sound of the blowing lungs. He felt his weakness, and the old bravado getting up, he stopt all of a sudden, and waited for me.

"Why, man," said I, "you have just to walk back again; so what's the use?"

"No use," he replied, doggedly; "only if you hadn't caught me I would have been well on to Dalkeith."

Plunging my hands into his coat-pocket, I pulled out a bundle of picklocks.

"Not cured yet?" said I.

"No," replied he, "and never will. You have spoiled a good job at Dalkeith with your d——d dodging."

"Are you a member of a Dalkeith society, too, Lang?" I retorted, good-naturedly.

"Something better," said he; "I might have had £10 in my pocket before morning, if you hadn't come between me and my game."

We began our walk homewards. I didn't require to take hold of him. We had measured our powers, and he knew he had no more chance in flight than in personal conflict, and he walked quietly enough. I would put my handcuffs to use, however, at the Gibbet Toll, to provide against the dangers of alleys favourable to a bolt. I remember I tried him on the soft parts, in regard to the society-box, reminding him that he was robbing the widow and the fatherless.

"Humph! what have I to do with the widow and the fatherless? I am an orphan myself, and there is a difference besides, for your widow and fatherless have friends, because they have characters, and I don't know but they are better cared for than I, who have neither the one nor the other. I am bound to a trade, as that trade is bound to me, and I must live or die by it. So there's no use for your blarney about widows and orphans. All you have to do is to take me up, and get me condemned and imprisoned, and I will be the same man when I come out."

No doubt he would; and why should I have doubted, who scarcely, in all my experience, could hold out my finger and say, "There's a man whom I have mended, and he is grateful to me for having been hard with him?" No wonder I am weary of my efforts at penal reformation.

I believe the nine months' imprisonment awarded

to these three desperate fellows only steeled them to dare the committal of crimes deserving transportation for as many years. How true it is, that the current of vice and criminality proceeds, both in its ebb and flow, on a "sliding scale".

Glossary

ash-bucket – bucket used for collecting ash

card-sharper – one who is skilful at playing or manipulating cards; one who makes a living by cheating at cards

flunkey – attendant or footman

gimmer – one-year-old ewe lamb

girnal – food storage chest

gudgeon – circular fitting (pivot or spindle, usually metal), fixed to a surface on which an object swings

gunwale – nautical term describing the top edge of the side of a boat

hied – to head (v.)

kail – colewort, cabbage, or borecole

lava streets – linked with the Vesuviennes *(see below)*

lieges – lord or sovereign to whom allegiance and service are due according to feudal law

muckle – much or many

peat-reek – the smoke of peat

prigging – petty thief or pickpocket

reset – to knowingly receive, handle or dispose of stolen goods

stirk – yearling heifer or bullock (six to twelve months old)

stots – bullocks

trulls – testicles

Vesuviennes – 19th-century French feminists' group